GW00859229

NURSES ...

the

Stories

We

Could

Tell

CANDIA CUMBERBATCH-LUCENIUS,
MHA/RN-Midwife/BSN/CPHM
with OTHER NURSES

Copyright © 2020 Candia Cumberbatch-Lucenius

All rights reserved. This book or any portion thereof
may not be reproduced or used in any manner whatsoever
without the express written permission of the publisher
except for the use of brief quotations in a book review

Printed in the United States of America

All rights reserved.

ISBN: 8575706168

ISBN-13: 979-8575706168

Rev. 1

Digital Inspirations

2402 Rambler Road

Wilmington, DE 19810

(302) 475-3013

www.Digital-Inspirations.press

* * *

Dedication

To God be the glory, I am thankful to God who divinely leads me every day, and without whom I am nothing.

This book is dedicated to nurses everywhere, including allied health staff. Nursing is not for the faint of heart and for those of us who have weathered the storm for years, I tip my hat to you.

When I started nursing in the seventies, my goal was just to take care of the sick – since that was all I knew or understood about nursing. By the end of my first year, I knew that was where I wanted to be – it felt like I was home, in my comfort zone. It took me several years to realize or even accept that I had followed my calling. What exactly is a 'calling'?

One online dictionary defines a 'calling' as "a strong urge toward a particular way of life or career: a vocation".

What really resonates with me as a spiritual woman is found in the Bible.

Ephesians 4:1 I therefore, the prisoner of the Lord, beseech you that ye walk worthy of the vocation wherewith ye are called,

That verse is telling me that I've been called by God Himself to walk according to the standard of His Word. Because of that, I felt like my nursing career was a part of my calling as a servant of the most High God.

"Nurses, The Stories We Could Tell" will take us on another journey of nurses and their individual experiences. After completing my book "A NURSES JOURNEY", I felt led to follow it up with stories from other nurses who I knew had some stories to tell. Please come along on this ride with us and take a look into the heart, humanity and soul of nurses.

To my husband and family, thanks for your support and love every day.

To my friends who have become an extension of my family, thanks for your love and support.

To nurses all over the world, we belong to a unique group of heroes. We comfort, take care of, coach and pray for those in our care. We've answered the call to do no harm but alleviate pain and assist with patients and their family's well-being. For many of us it's a thank-less job, waking up at the crack of dawn, working way into the night or doing the midnight/grave-yard shift. We've had sleepless days and nights; we've worked overtime when needed without complaining – well, maybe a little but we did it over and over again.

God bless each of you, I am proud and honored to be called a 'Nurse'.

Candia Cumberbatch-Lucenius - -MHA/RN-Midwife/BSN/CPHM/Master Herbalist/Health Minister; Director and Founder of The Women of Virtue women's group; Owner of Healing and Comforting Hearts

Acknowledgments

Special mention to some of my special friends and colleagues as well as my sister who took the time to contribute to the book 'Nurses … The Stories We Could Tell'.

Kathleen Cumberbatch RN/CM/UR Manager

Mrs. Diana M Yarde; SEN; RN

Nadene R. Taniguchi, BSN, RN, CCM, CNLCP, PAHM

Esther Charles, LPN. Ottawa, Canada

Jacintha Brouet, RN/Midwife/Community Health Nurse

Jacinta Serieux-Fontenelle MPH, BSN, RN, CNOB

Bernadette Springer, RN/Midwife/Community Health Nurse/Women Affairs Officer/Health Clinic Administrator

Christel Roberts/RN/Dialysis Nurse

Cleo Charles-Phillips, RN-Midwife/OB Nurse

Table of Contents

BIOGRAPHY

Candia Cumberbatch-Lucenius is a Registered Nurse with over forty years of experience in every area of nursing. Everyone who knows me have heard me say Midwifery has and always will be my most cherished area of nursing. From the first day, I walked into the classroom, it felt so comfortable – like a perfect fit. By the second week our instructor was already calling me her assistant, and I sailed through the program completing it top of the class. This was followed by several years of training future midwife's, caring for the patient's before, during and post-delivery as well as the care of the newborn. This experience included the delivery of hundreds of babies, from normal SVD's (spontaneous vaginal deliveries, to breech deliveries to twin deliveries. Each one as rewarding as the last. Candia received her Registered Nurse/ Midwife Diploma in St. Lucia, followed by a BSN, MHA and was inducted into the Honor Society for Nurses for her academic achievements and dedication to nursing. When she decided to transition away from bedside nursing she worked as a Case Manager and Utilization review Manager for several major managed care companies, a HEDIS Nurse Reviewer, Nurse Auditor, and a Clinical Quality Nurse Analyst. In these roles she has been an Assistant Director of Nursing, Nurse Manager, Supervisor, Team Lead, and Project Manager.

Candia is a published poet and author of five books, one a

book of inspirational poetry – Pearls at the Throne of Grace, and two others – Flowers for Mama and Reflections of Life to My Younger Self, which contain contributions from friends and family. She recently completed her fourth and fifth books – one a daily devotional and the other a memoir which chronicles her calling as a nurse. 'Nurses, The Stories We Could Tell' also contains contributions from other nurses sharing some of their nursing experiences. Another proud accomplishment is having her work published in a well-known Medical Magazine for continuing education credits for medical professionals.

Always having a strong interest in Natural Health and Healing, Candia has refocused her nursing career to highlight the body as a self-healing system, is now a Health Minister, a Master Herbalist, and is finalizing her Doctorate degree in Natural Health and Healing.

Another passion in her life is studying the Bible and learning how to make it a practical part of her daily life. She believes that full healing can only be accomplished by complete wholeness which includes mind, body & spirit. As a Natural Health Consultant, Coach and Health Minister, Candia incorporates all these aspects.

In 2009, Candia founded and still is the Director the Women of Virtue (WOV) group which is based on Proverbs 31:12-31. It is a safe place where women come together to encourage, support, and uplift one another which includes fun times, prayer times, self-care, rejuvenating times, and getaways.

Candia recently started her business Healing and Comforting Hearts, which focuses on bringing comfort to those dealing with difficult diagnoses, chronic debilitating illnesses, and to those who've lost loved ones. Comfort and Prayer boxes are customized to meet the need and include one of Candis's original poems, individualized for the person(s).

ONCE A NURSE ALWAYS A NURSE

How do you spell NURSE?

NURTURING:
We care for, administer medications,
feed them, and listen.

UNSELFISH:
Running to help one another when
the load seems too much.

RESILIENT:
Long nights, overtime shifts,
many days with no lunch or potty break.

STRONG:
Lifting and turning even the heaviest
of patients, making sure they are comfortable.

EMPATHETIC:
Choosing to put ourselves in one's place
and being understanding.

NURSES - that is who we are.

To all nurses around the globe.

Let us celebrate each other.

*Candia Cumberbatch-Lucenius, MHA / RN-Midwife / BSN / CPHM /
Master Herbalist / Health Minister*

WHAT ELSE CAN I DO?

It was an evening shift and I was assigned to a gynecology floor (non-surgical). She was only in her seventies, which at the time as an eighteen-year-old student nurse, to me seemed old. The diagnosis cancer of the vulva, with metastasis to the cervix. And my word, what pain she was in- we could hear her scream from down the hall.

When I met her, she was receiving morphine every two hours and paracetamol for the breakthrough pain. Nothing helped and I truly felt helpless and asked myself every day, "What else can I do?" Seitz baths every four hours helped soothe some of the pain and she might dose off for fifteen minutes after that, but then she was up again groaning and crying out in pain.

Through it all, she was one of the nicest patients I had, respectfully and quietly requesting help with her pleas of "Nurse, can you help me please?" Every one of us had a hard time dealing with such raw pain and pleas for help, and we did everything we could and were almost relieved when she finally passed away. We were sad and grieved with her family but welcomed the fact that she was no longer in such excruciating pain and there was nothing else we could do.

Candia Cumberbatch-Lucenius, MHA / RN-Midwife / BSN / CPHM

ONLY GOD KNOWS WHY

Saturday.......Who wants to, or even likes to work on a weekend? Least of all me. Those days were my fun days. I had a life! I also had made a commitment to be a NURSE first. So, I got dressed in my royal blue dress put on my white apron and brownish stockings and white shoes. Ready to head off to work.... wait, cannot leave without my cap! Sparkling white starched so stiff that it felt like if you squooshed it together it would break into a million pieces. Taking a deep breath and sending out a small prayer for a peaceful day at work. I walked over to the emergency room. This was my first year as a Registered Nurse and I was proud of me.

As I walked through the doors of "Casualty" (another name for our ED in St. Lucia), I saw my favorite nurses to work with was on duty today as well. God was answering my payers. Then in walked Sister G. She was the sweetest, most understanding, most knowledgeable, manager (to me.....I was a very good nurse, but not with the sweetest personality) To my patient's, I was the BEST, to my coworkers, they were like "Not her again! ...Jealousy????

We got report from the night shift and accepted assignments from sister G. I was assigned to the three exam rooms closer to the front desk. I was a tad bummed cause, first "casualty "would be coming to me. I accepted graciously, however, and sat at the front desk at the entrance of the ED with the rest of the Nurses and Nurses assistants. We talked about everything under the sun, including marriage, dating, going out, and children.

Doctor 24 walked in, "Look like I could have stayed in my bed, huh. Nobody coming in here today." Now all nurses know that these are the WORST words to say on a seemingly quiet day. Three minutes later, in walked Mrs. T. She was a regular "Customer", a diabetic who had a diabetic ulcer on left leg. It had gotten so bad, that her doctor did not think she was actually changing the dressing as instructed at home. So, she was instructed to have it cleaned and dressed at the hospital every day, so it could be monitored. In tow was her granddaughter Liza. She was a chatter box and we all loved her. She brightened everyone's day…. regardless of what mood you were in. Today she was especially chattery as she was promised a baby brother by her pregnant mom (who was not accompanying them, as "she needed bedrest".) Liza chattered on and on, about being excited to be a big sister and she knows how to bottle feed because she has been practicing with her dolls. Then she's going to teach him how to crawl and walk and talk and as soon as he is big enough, they are going to get a football and their dad would teach them how to play football. However, as Liza put it "I am a big girl and will have to wear pants, so my dress does not blow up. "Girls are little ladies" she informed.

I completed the dressing change with adding caution to Mrs. T about her diet, exercise, medication and lastly giving a compliment on her oh so beautiful and smart granddaughter. She thanked us profusely took Liza's hand and with much encouragement and promises that "of course, I will bring you with me tomorrow", they left.

We were all in AWE of them both. She walked away skipping and I am sure talking her grandma's ear off. Sister G broke the ice as we all sat in silence. I'm sure with our own thoughts on different aspects of our different life's. "you know" she said. "Children like her do not usually live very long, they are just too intelligent and happy for this world. She is an angel, and God will probably take her before she gets too old to pick up on the evil of this world". Us nurses were not happy to hear that, but we all believed it, just did not want to and did not admit it.

"Well, I will go make sure I cleaned up sufficiently after my dressing change, I said" Then I heard the ambulance. "Oh no" I said, "but this one is not mine; I had the first, this is yours nurse R". "I know", Nurse R said. "Here we go". The ambulance pulled up and out jumped 4 firemen. One had what seemed to be a small child covered in mud and the other person a lady covered in mud on a stretcher. We stared in horror as the realization hit that this was Mrs. T and Liza.

Mrs. T was rushed to the operating room and Liza was placed

on one of the stretcher's in my exam room. In unison we asked," what happened?" The fireman with tears in his eyes said "a car went off the road and hit them both clear over the bridge into the muddy river. When they pulled them out Liza was still holding her Grandma's hand, but her body was limp, and it appears that her neck is broken. Dr. 24 came rushing out and started CPR, Nurse R attempted to start an IV. Sister G was sitting on a chair crying her heart out. I was holding Liza's hand and knew. There was nothing left to do. Nurse R looked at me and Dr. 24 walked to the outside. There was not a dry eye in the ED – the doctor, nurses, firemen, nursing assistants, everyone, cried and simultaneously prayed for the little one's departed soul.

Mrs. T's Leg had to be amputated (not the one with the diabetic ulcer though), and she was admitted to ICU, for additional injuries. Finally, Mrs. T pulled through, Liza's Mom had a baby boy, born prematurely but healthy! Dad was inconsolable and had to be sedated for a bit. Me, I can never forget!

This was admittedly one of the most horrifying times in all of my nursing career.

Kathleen Cumberbatch RN/CM/UR Manager

BIOGRAPHY: Kathleen L. Cumberbatch is one of six siblings born on the Caribbean island of St. Lucia. After graduating from High school, Kathleen started working as a teacher's aide, while she tried to figure out what she wanted to do with her life. Shortly after she became a single

Mom to her beautiful daughter, and after being encouraged by her sister who was a Registered Nurse, and several others, Kathleen went to nursing school and became a Registered Nurse as well.

Several years into nursing, Kathleen got restless and relocated to the U.S. where she held several jobs in various hospitals in Brooklyn and Manhattan in NY.

Kathleen married and relocated to Baltimore where she continued her nursing career at one of the most prestigious hospitals there. After about 30 plus years of bedside nursing, and relocating to enjoy warmer weather, more like what she was accustomed to, Kathleen worked several different positions in a well-known hospital in Florida. For the last several years Kathleen has been a Case Manager, and Utilization Review Manager and a budding author.

MY ADOPTIVE FAMILY

The year was 1991. It was my first ward as a new Graduate Nurse after successfully completing the Associate Degree (RN) 5A, the ward where I was allocated, was one of two wards on the Private wing. It was a Surgical ward and 6A was the Medical. Each ward contained 15 private rooms.

Even though I wasn't new to nursing, I was still nervous because of the feedback from nurses on the general wards, where I had done my clinicals as a student nurse.

Prior to this, I had done the State Enrolled Nurse (SEN) certificate in England and on my return, worked in a few private clinics. This was different though because I was now at the Public General Hospital, which was also a teaching institution and where students came from all over the West Indies to train, both doctors and nurses. It was the only general hospital on the island and had a capacity of 600 beds.

I felt nervous here because of the doctors` reputation for perfection and their being quick to ball you out in public if you messed up.
As I was being orientated to the ward, this was confirmed by the nurse. She assured me that once I followed their instructions carefully and updated them on the progress of their patients, I should not have any problems. What I learnt though, is that each doctor had little idiosyncrasies that they liked to follow. E.g. on dressing the patients` wounds, one

doctor would prefer Red Lotion, one Betadine and another Eusol.

I had always prided myself on doing my best at all times and planned to double my efforts in this situation. As time went by, I soon had these things down packed and started to enjoy the ward, spending more time with the patients every chance I got. Whilst making rounds, I gathered from the patients that even though the care was excellent, they sometimes felt lonely because they did not get to see anyone except the doctors and nurses until visiting time. I vowed to myself that I would check them more often.

On this occasion, one of my admissions was an elderly gentleman who had major abdominal surgery for colon cancer. He appeared quite ill and was connected to several tubes, including a colostomy bag. He required a lot of care. I always made it a practice to make a round at the end of my shift to say goodbye to the patients and wish them a goodnight's rest.

The ward always seemed busy. Patients were constantly being admitted or discharged. Nurses didn't have a lot of time to engage them in long conversations. I used the visiting hours which were 12pm – 1pm and 4.30pm – 8pm, to chat with those patients who didn't have visitors. The elderly gentleman, Mr. Granger, was one of those, since his family visited in the evening. I would engage him in small talk and encourage him to be positive. He grew to like my visits and always requested that I came again soon.

One evening I was on the 1pm – 9pm shift and during visiting time, I was called to his room. When I got there, his wife, son and two daughters were present, and he introduced me to them. He said, "this nurse is very good to me. You must never forget her." I was very surprised and humbled because I didn't expect that. I usually treated all my patients the same and there were other caring nurses on the ward too, so I didn't want to be singled out. I told them that much but he wouldn't have it any other way.

Mr. Granger spent three weeks on the ward before he was discharged with an appointment to return for a second surgery to re-anastomose the bowel. (replace the bowel in its original position). He returned three weeks later for surgery after which he was admitted to ICU due to a bowel infection. I am sorry to say that due to his weakened immune system, he succumbed to his illness.

I attended the funeral and offered my sympathy to the family. They promised to keep in touch.

A few weeks later his wife called to see how I was doing. We had a lengthy conversation and one of the things she said was to understand that I was now part of the family, and from now on I was to call her 'mummy.'

Again, this was another humbling moment. The first being my introduction to the family and now my adoption into the family. The children also embraced me as their sibling.

To make a long story short, it is now twenty-eight years that we have known one another and throughout that period, we have shared wonderful moments together. Mummy passed away in November 2019 and I would say that she was the best mother a girl could have, since my biological mother died when I was only fifteen months old.

From this I've learnt that it doesn't matter the status of the person or the fact that you are being paid for what you do, being genuinely kind and caring to all is what matters most.

Mrs. Diana M Yarde, RN; SEN

BIOGRAPHY: Diana Yarde is a retired SEN, SRN (State Enrolled Nurse/ State Registered Nurse) who lives in Barbados, West Indies. She is a wife, mother to a grown son and friend to many. She loves God and people and gets much pleasure in seeing them happy.

She spends most of her time working for the church. Diana founded the Health Guild with a membership of sixteen persons who look after the physical needs of the elderly in the congregation and its shut-ins by hosting clinicals at church and visiting the house bound.

MERRY CHRISTMAS IN ICU

I have been a Registered Nurse for now 43 years. My experience has included various specialties such as Intensive Care; Post-Anesthesia Care; Case Management; Utilization Review; Revenue Integrity; Consulting; and now my current vocation of working as a Life Care Planner. I have so many memories and stories over the years. Some so sad, they can't be told, some so funny they shouldn't be told. As a very young nurse I began searching for a specialty where I could learn and grow and make an impact. I was sent to several units as most of us were and pretty much disliked them all. Obstetrics wasn't for me, Medical Surgical wasn't for me, and Pediatrics surely wasn't for me. One day I was assigned to the Intensive Care Unit at the first hospital I ever worked in. ICU? Why would any person in management permit this to happen or on a personal level, do this to me? I now know how staffing ratios etc. sent me there but at the time, all I knew was fear. And fear that should be!

Intimidation is not a normal experience in my life but for sure on that day, I was intimidated to the point of being scared to death. The nurses and doctors were buzzing about with an expertise that I could only dream of having. They were using terms I have never heard of and making decisions at breakneck speed. And, by the way, no one was particularly nice or welcoming to me. Who could blame them? Here I was sent to fill a quota. with no experience, little knowledge and essentially of no help whatsoever. My only asset was my willingness to learn and stay out of the way.

Fast forward to a couple of years later (yes, you are forced to learn quickly in ICU). I had taken additional education, was mentored by a couple of fabulous nurses and learned my craft well. I worked day and night and grew to love the environment. Intensive care was my specialty, I was damn good at it and became a respected member of the team. All of this leads me to this story that was not only life changing to me as a nurse but as a person.

One Christmas eve (for real) I was working with a minimal staff as was the norm during holiday time. We had strategically planned for the 10-bed unit to be nearly empty except for the critical patients who were not stable enough to be moved to the step-down unit. Our staffing was lean at best (and I am being kind here). At that time, LPNs were permitted to practice in ICU. Staffing that night consisted of me (RN), one LPN, a resident physician covering the unit and the Emergency Department. We had two (2) acutely ill patients. One patient, "Mrs. G" had suffered a myocardial infarction the day before. She was stable with labs trending downwards. The only other nurse in the unit requested to break for dinner. All seemed quiet, so why not? After all, what could happen in 30 minutes with two stable patients? Guess again.

Mrs. G requested a bedpan which I provided and left the room to allow her privacy. As I walked back to the supply room a short distance away, my mind wandered to the fact that it had been a few minutes since Mrs. G was placed on the bedpan. Was it three minutes or five minutes? No alarms were sounding, everything looked fine. However, my heart began to race. I knew instinctively what was happening. Mrs. G was extending her infarct. Urgently, I ran to the room to find Mrs. G fading quickly. There was no need to wait another second and I called a code. Great, a call for help from whom? A resident covering the entire hospital and no one else. Mrs. G's blood pressure was alarmingly low, and I knew I needed to get some medications going. Problem was she had one peripheral line only and the medication choice at the time had to be run separately. Thanks to my mentors I was taught to start a tiny infant line when minimal vein access was available. But where? This lady was is her late 70's and all the veins in her hand were not great. I decided the foot was the only viable option. It was then I placed a tiny butterfly catheter into Mrs. G's foot and started the drip. She responded. The next hours proved to be amazing. Of course, the covering internist turned the event into his personal crisis. How could this happen to me on Christmas Eve? You are all familiar with the whine.

All turned out well for Mrs. G. She recovered and was discharged to home. I was pleased.

Fast forward to several months later when I was visiting a friend for a planned cycling event. Just like that my friend's neighbor, Mr. G. who lived next door to my friend appeared. He walked towards the porch and asked if I remembered him. Of course, I remembered him and asked him how his wife was doing. He responded that she was doing better. By now, I am feeling a bit proud. Suddenly the conversation changed. Mr. G told me how his wife had been experiencing chest discomfort and finally had an imaging study that showed her sternum had been fractured. I expressed my concern and wished them both well. He then stated he ought to sue me for hurting his wife. Sue ME? I was so astounded. When I finally gathered my thoughts, I approached Mr. G and said, please feel free to seek the advice of an attorney but know this, without my help that night you would not have had your wife for one more day. I sincerely hope her sternum pain is not crippling. Mrs. G lived another nine years.

Nadene R. Taniguchi, BSN, RN, CCM, CNLCP, PAHM

BIOGRAPHY: Nadene R. Taniguchi has been a registered nurse since 1976. She currently works as a certified nurse life care planner.

Nadene R. Taniguchi, BSN, RN, CCM, CNLCP, PAHM has forty years of experience in the hospital and insurance industries, with expertise in acute and post-acute case management, utilization review and compliance with federal regulations. Nadene has spearheaded projected to improve emergency department services, patient safety and patient satisfaction.

Nadene currently works as a life care planner with BalaCare Solutions.

Education and Certifications

• BSN, St. Joseph's College, Standish, Maine

• CCM, Certified Case Manager

• CNLCP, Certified Nurse Life Care Planner

•PAHM, Professional, Academy of Healthcare Management

STUDENT NURSE and BEYOND

As a student nurse in the early '80's', my first employ was at a senior's home. I was very nervous and apprehensive about doing elderly care, wondering if I could make a difference in their quality of life. But I soon realized when I looked in their eyes, these were people with their own fears and stories. They were depending on me to help them get through each day with dignity, care and compassion.

I soon saw the isolation and loneliness, felt by so many seniors through 30 years of my career in geriatric nursing. It was very challenging at times. I realize more than just giving meds and physical care, what made the difference was a kind word, a smile, a gentle touch, brought joy and comfort to my clients. I knew this was my calling and I made a difference.

On a lighter note there was a lady called Mary who resided at the senior's home I worked at.

On one occasion I made the mistake of addressing her as Mrs. she promptly corrected me, that she was Miss, but she didn't miss a thing, she enjoyed her life.

One of the many lessons I learned over my years in the nursing care of the elderly is that aside from the medical and physical care, which is vital and important, our clients want to feel respected. They want to be heard and seen as valued members of society. Many feel overlooked because of their age and they do not want their advanced age to diminish their contributions or their worth as significant human beings.

Esther Charles, LPN. Ottawa, Canada

BIOGRAPHY: Esther grew up in Ottawa Canada with her twelve siblings, where she still resides with her significant other of many years, her two daughters and grandchildren, many nieces and nephews and her mother.

SHORT STORIES

The following are a few short stories as told to me by one of my very dear friends.

Some of my memories of my nursing experiences have stuck with me over the years and still remind me of why I've enjoyed nursing.

MOTHER / BABY

I was assigned to an outpatient health center not too close to any hospitals. Usually these assignments meant you had to be on call after hours and overnight. It was two am when I was awakened by a knocking on the front door. A middle-aged man stood there and said his wife was in labor and needed assistance, stating also there was no way she could make it to the health center since they had no form of transportation.

I quickly got dressed and followed him, led by the light from the health center, which grew dimmer and dimmer as we walked further away. He then turned on a small kerosene lamp which flickered gently as we walked into the deep darkness of the night along a rough unpaved road. We arrived to find the young lady still writhing in pain and just about ready to deliver – 9cm by vaginal exam.

I prepped her, administered a Demerol IM to ease her contractions, and started an IV. It wasn't long before she was ready to push, and yes, I did all that and delivered her by the flickering light of that small kerosene lamp. The delivery of the placenta was uneventful, with the uterus contracted adequately, bleeding normal, and I was able to turn my attention to the assessment and clean-up of the healthy baby boy with great lungs. You guessed it; he was not too happy being disturbed from his warm watery home.

Over the years I have had several patients deliver at home unattended and walk into the clinic with baby wrapped in a towel, some with the placenta still attached, several with the placenta not delivered. The process to care for the mother post-delivery and the newborn is as mentioned above. The pediatrician on call is usually summoned to examine the baby. The mother is given a dose of antibiotics and sent home with a prescription to continue it for a few days.

POST STROKE

Another memorable incident was when I went to the home of a post-CVA patient. The caretaker stated she had removed her naso-gastric (NG) tube and the family was concerned for her nutritional wellbeing, and requested I re-insert the feeding tube. After her stroke the patient was left with severe neurological and physical deficits. Her speech remained slurred for a long time and she had difficulty swallowing on her own – hence the NG tube.

On my arrival, I found the woman to have good swallowing and gag reflexes, so I suggested the caretaker continue to try feeding her liquids and advance to soft foods as tolerated. The family was very excited about the progress and very thankful.

THE HOMELESS AND ELDERLY

The struggle to care for the homeless and elderly is hard and tugs at your heart strings. The homeless are usually brought in by ambulance, emaciated and unkempt. They are kept in house for 48 – 72 hours or more sometimes depending on the severity of their condition. They are fed, re-hydrated with intravenous (IV) fluids and cleaned up, dressed in clothes that have been donated by the public and discharged.

While working in the clinic or health center another one of my responsibilities was home visits (much like a Home Health Nurse. One such visit was to an elderly gentleman, if I remember correctly was around 82-83 years old. He lived alone and had no family, apart from our weekly visits he didn't see too many people. I would take a nursing assistant along with me who assisted in giving him his bath, dressing and grooming him and making sure he had a hot meal, with leftovers for several days. Our elderly friend lived for two years under our care and it was sad to say goodbye when he was gone.

* * *

THE NON-COMPLIANT

We got to know this special class of patients really well in the hospital — we call them non-compliant. They are our COPD (Chronic Obstructive Pulmonary Disease), who in spite of warnings from their doctors, advice from the nurses, and severe shortness of breath continued their pack a day, down from two pack a day smoking habit. And, did I mention they are on home oxygen (O2) — two liters, some four in severe cases. Re-admission is inevitable due to exacerbation, sometimes needing to be vented and still it doesn't end until the end.

Then we have the diabetics, on insulin who insist of having that piece of cake that is just too irresistible or that coconut bread, or sweet potato pie. They make no dietary changes even after education and coaching. Eventually, they are re-admitted time and time again in ketoacidosis or with a blood sugar level of 500 plus.

Sorry to say these are the ones expecting a miracle cure from the medical team while refusing to adhere to any advice. No amount of education or coaching has proven successful. And so, we grieve with the families.

While we're at it, how about our dialysis patients, who we get to know really well- they're in twice, sometimes three days a week for dialysis. The care is chronic and long term, and you want to help make it better. These are generally non-compliant Diabetics, who even after re-education and informing them that their kidney function was declining – 30%, 25%, even as low as 15% of kidney function left, remained non-compliant. There's not too much you can do but repeat the instructions and pray they will comply before it's too late.

NURSE AND PHLEBOTOMIST

One patient of mine a young lady no more than about twenty-five years was admitted after she had collapsed. She was admitted with a Hemoglobin of 2, history of fibroids and severe vaginal bleeding. Several unsuccessful attempts were made by the doctors to start an IV and draw her blood. My attempts too were unsuccessful; we were not able to find a vein initially, and when we did were not able to get one drop of blood out of it. We lost her about 2 hours after she was admitted. Another senseless, heart-breaking loss.

I DIDN'T GET TO HELP HER

It was about five pm, when the screeching sound of a vehicle caught our attention. I was making rounds, as the evening supervisor and was just walking into the emergency room. "Please help my wife; we need help!" I heard the desperate pleas of the man as I approached. As I got closer, it was followed by a more feeble cry from a young woman, "I need oxygen, please; I need oxygen." Then, "she cannot breathe," the young man stated. I walked into the room and started to get the oxygen ready, but by the time I got to her lying there on the stretcher, she had taken her last breath. A later autopsy showed she had multiple Pulmonary Emboli. I never got to help her.

The pleasant side of all these sad stories help bring some light and a smile to my face. I'm walking down the street, or into a supermarket, maybe climbing the steps to church and someone will help me if I cannot remember them. It may be anywhere from 10-12 years later and the face is familiar, but the memory is vague. They then remind me of the loved one I care for, or maybe themselves, the baby I delivered who is now in grade five or six, or some other memory, which would include hugs, and many thanks. It makes it worthwhile.

Jacintha Brouet, RN/Midwife; District Nurse

LESSONS FROM MY PATIENTS
Copyright©9/2019 JSFontenelle

Nursing has been an important part of my life for over forty years. It has played a vital role in helping me become the person I am today. When I was growing up in the tropical island of St Lucia, fresh out of high school in search of a fulfilling career, I chose nursing because it offered an opportunity to work with people, and help others while keeping active, for I knew I was not interested in a 'desk job'. Having observed and listened to my older sister, who was a senior nurse at the time, I knew enough to understand that this was a challenging profession. I was unaware of how versatile and unpredictable it could be, nor did I imagine how difficult it actually was. Yet, those are the very aspects of nursing that kept me in the profession for over 40 years.

If I were to think in illustrative format, I would picture my chosen profession of nursing as a special room with a wall full of outfits to choose from. I learned about that room during the theoretical part of my training and then entered it during the practical training in the clinical setting. In the clinical setting, I met the flesh and blood patient who I had heard so much about. The patient who was the focus of the profession, who I looked forward to meeting so I could demonstrate what I had learnt. The patient that is undefinable, unpredictable and the ultimate challenge because he or she comes in such varied ages, shapes, sizes, personalities, characters etc. and in spite of an apparent excellent theoretical education reminds you that there is always more to learn.

Throughout my training in the clinical setting, I was required to try on at least 80% of those outfits for size and fit. Some were too small or too big, some felt somewhat uncomfortable and not quite me. Mostly they felt new, strange but exciting. Sometimes, I felt like I could live the rest of my life wearing a particular outfit, like the one for Maternal and Child. It made me feel excited, fulfilled, challenged, and filled with anticipation with every new opportunity it afforded. I could not imagine boredom while wearing it. I could see myself growing and learning with it and all the while contributing in ways that I could only dream of.

This was my experience in my early years as a nurse. During my clinical training, I realized that psychiatry (the big outfit) was not a fit for me. It was too big and uncomfortable. Pediatrics (the small outfit) was also not a good fit, maybe too tight and painful. Overall, I was comfortable with and enjoyed the other specialties during my training. Then I did the maternity rotation and I knew, like Goldilocks in the classic story, that I had found just the right fit.

I loved everything about caring for the woman and child. It was demanding, it was versatile, it was fulfilling; it was exciting work that impacted me on a professional and personal level. At 21, I found myself caring for pregnant women who were much older and more mature than I, some were old enough to be my mother. As the midwife, I was the provider who was primarily responsible for their care from conception to post postpartum and beyond. A very significant role that was quite humbling, I had no choice but to mature very quickly. In addition, as I became a Community Health Nurse, I became the primary provider for the whole family. It was an experience that helped me grow and develop both as a woman and as a nurse and kept me working as a clinical nurse at the bedside for over 35 years. It was incredible. The experiences I had, the amazing people I met, both colleagues and patients, cannot be fully described.

This was a remarkable fit for me and helped me grow in confidence as I faced the challenges of new and changing roles. Now that I have moved on to be a clinical instructor/writer, I hope to help my students understand that this was not just a profession to me, it was an important life choice. It not only helped me grow, but also guided me on my life's journey of creatively juggling my profession, my family, and my spiritual life so that I could become the person I am today. It provided a means to have a positive impact on the life of others and contribute to the advancement of the profession.

The effect that my patients had on me was the most significant aspect of my nursing career. This impact has changed how I view myself and the people I care for. As a result, I have been challenged to become a more effective nurse and a kinder person. One of the most memorable lessons I have learned was from a young lady during my first 10 years in nursing. Many a nurse can relate to the experience of having a patient who complained and complained with no apparent cause. Well, this was one such patient who helped shape my practice of nursing. As the Community Health Nurse-Midwife this young lady was one of the patients attending the prenatal clinic. She started her visits in the first trimester (three months) of her first pregnancy. She was a very pleasant and cooperative patient. At first her pregnancy seemed to progress well, then the complaints started. I tried everything, counseling, painkillers, and referrals to the obstetrician with no resolution. I sometimes thought that she may be, 'putting on' since her pain was so unusual (she described it as constant) and nothing seemed to work. All seemed normal except her constant complaint of pain. Since ultrasound technology was not available at that time in the island, we had to wait until the third trimester to use x-ray for further diagnosis. A fetus could be palpated, and seemed to be growing normally, but her pain persisted. Strangely, she was not unduly bothered by palpation (examination by touch) and did not seem to experience any unusual abdominal tenderness. The obstetrician agreed that he did not notice anything abnormal with her exams. Her diagnosis was, 'unexplained pain'. By the third trimester, I was convinced that something was really wrong; even though the pregnancy was progressing normally, the pain was worsening, and I concluded that she could not be faking this reaction to pain. After consulting with the obstetrician, we decided the best course of action was to perform an x-ray to try to identify the cause of this persistent, worsening pain. Based on the x-ray result, we discovered the cause of this persistent pain – Abdominal Pregnancy. This type of pregnancy is rare and presents grave risks to both the mother and her unborn baby. Thankfully the diagnosis was timely, both mom and baby survived and they both thrived after surgery. Not only did this young lady make an impact but I was able to be part of a very rare occurrence in pregnancy; an abdominal pregnancy that results in a healthy mother and newborn.

The profound lessons I learned from this experience were:

- never dismiss a patient's complaints.

- never conclude that, the unusual is 'in their head'.

- there is always something new to learn so be an enthusiastic learner.

- listen to your patients, they live with their body 24/7.

These lessons have helped me countless times in critical situations over the years; times when listening to the patient has helped me decide on a course of action that minimized wasted time and helped the team focus on an effective, efficient and successful course of action.

The experience described above laid the cornerstone for developing a foundational attitude of empathy combined with sensitivity and respect for my patient. Listening to them has helped me understand more deeply, that they don't give up their personhood during the process of ill-health which requires them to seek help at a healthcare facility. Each patient is a unique individual, a living breathing person, who can teach those of us who have control over their care – who they often believe know so much more than they do. I learned that it is wise to listen carefully to their voice, often muffled by stereotypical trappings, for they all have an exclusive story which, when heard, increases our ability to effectively care for them.

Nursing also offered an opportunity to learn from the life and experiences of others and thereby better understand my strengths and weaknesses. This helped me develop mentally, emotionally and spiritually as I practiced what I learned and applied it not in caring for my patients but also to myself and my family. Unexpected, unplanned challenges, both personal and professional prevented me from developing an attitude of complacency.

The following is an excerpt of a poem written from the perspective of the patients who, over the past few decades, I have had the honor to care for and to share in their joys, sorrows, successes and frustrations. People who have touched my life in profound ways and taught me so very much!

Jacinta Serieux-Fontenelle MPH, BSN, RN, CNOB

* * *

THE PATIENT

I come to you for help, carrying with me my physical woes;

Taking along my invisible baggage, my personality, my prejudices, my all.

Please don't look at that suitcase and think that is all I own.

Know that it is only the outward symbol of the load I carry within.

Please do not take personally my sometimes-unfriendly response,

To your kind and caring acts.

Do not misunderstand my apparent ungratefulness to your selfless and efficient care.

Please remember that I come to you because I need your help.

I need to rely on you at this time, for I am helpless on my own.

I may never take the time to express my gratitude for your

care and concern;

But please don't hold it against me, for life's setbacks have so discouraged me;

That I can barely hold my own.

Just remember that your small acts of kindness and concern

Are like rays of light in my darkness.

If I make it out of the depths, it will be in large part to those rays,

Lighting, encouraging, healing my shattered soul..........

You may never hear my thank you, but rest assured it is there.

Deep down this abyss of pain and trials, which you may not quite understand.

I hope one day to be able to express it, then this is what I will say,

"Thank you for your patience when my frustration and anxiety,

Have made your task much more difficult and challenging.

Thank you for your understanding, for seeing beyond the moment.

Thank you for your perseverance in spite of me.

Thank you for the dedication that helps you make a difference;

But if I can't say it this side of heaven, maybe someday you will see

How your ray of sunshine lighted up my way."

My patients taught me so much that is difficult to express in just words. I can only say in summary, "they taught me that it is impossible to know the depth of the human soul; that the virtues of honesty, perseverance, love, kindness, determination and understanding come clothed in the most unlikely outerwear."

Jacinta Serieux-Fontenelle MPH, BSN, RN, CNOB

BIOGRAPHY: Jacinta was born in the beautiful Caribbean island of St Lucia. A professional nurse for over forty years, she has worked in a variety of settings and in the countries of St Lucia and the U.S.A. Her specialty of women's health started as a nurse-midwife in St Lucia and continued as a Certified Inpatient Obstetric Nurse in the U.S. She is now pursuing a career in writing and speaking while working as an adjunct clinical nurse instructor with the University of Delaware. Jacinta has been published in a Nursing magazine and The Upper Room Devotional, and coauthored in a few titles such as, 'Short and Sweet Takes the Fifth.' Her first book entitled, 'Contemporary Psalms; 365 Daily Reflections, was published in book and kindle form in 2019. Writing has always been an important part of her life, often expressed in poetry and short stories. Some of her interests include reading, needlework and gardening. One of 13 children, she places great value on family as one of God's greatest gift in her life and strives to cherish that special gift. A mother of three, she presently resides in the state of Delaware with her husband and two of her three children.

MORE THAN JUST DIALYSIS

My name is Christel and I got into the medical field later in my life. I had already had four kids and my husband noticed that I needed to do something for myself. When I had gotten married to him a single mom with two boys, I had mentioned wanting to maybe become a nurse. I had been a CNA as a single mom with two boys, but I wanted to try for that little girl before I focused on becoming a nurse. After having a little girl than another boy my husband encouraged me to focus on myself for once and do something for me. That is when I went to Nursing school. Having to get my pre- requisites and move forward. I graduated as a nurse in 2011 at the age of 46.

It took a while to land that first job, because I had not worked in the medical field for a few years and I had gone through school part time taking a little longer than most people. I finally landed a job in home healthcare taking care of children at home and in school, but I continued wanting something different even though I enjoyed my clients very much. I landed a job in dialysis. This was not a field I had ever thought of working in and had really never heard of renal failure until I took the class in nursing school. Still it had not been on the top of my list, but it did sound interesting and different.

Your kidney is like a filter I tell people, it filters our blood, cleaning it. Without it your blood builds toxins which if not removed will end one's life. A Dialysis nurse oversees the treatment of the patient in a chronic clinic. They have to check each patient after they are put on the machine and make sure the machine is set up right, and running the right treatment prescribed by their Physician. These treatments can run 3 to 4 or more hours. The first 12 weeks of being a dialysis nurse is training as a technician. The technicians are the medical aids that have been trained how to care for these patients. You learn how to set the machines up, how to string the tubing needed to withdraw and return the patient's blood, the dialyzer filter used for that patient and priming the machine to get it ready, how to keep the client safe, and having a sterile field while attaching the patient to the machine. There are also different techniques used to attach the client to the machine that one needs to know how perform.

Another particularly important step is making sure the client is as comfortable as can be. that they have everything they need for their treatment, the TV and their headphones, a book if they want to read. The Dialysis nurse over sees all the patients in their area depending on the size of the clinic - anywhere from 10 to 14 patients. They need to know the techs job as well as their own job. If one of the tech's calls out and there is a full house the nurse is then a tech and a nurse. The nurse checks each client making sure they are attached to the machine ok and the machine is running the proper treatment that was prescribed. It also helps to be a little mechanically savvy when it comes to working with these machines.

In dialysis the patient must sit in a recliner not moving too much due to being attached to the machine. The treatment only cleans 20 % to 25% of the patient's blood, but this is enough to help the body keep working. Some of the things that can occur during treatment is the patient can have difficulties with their blood pressure, trouble with their hook up site bleeding or getting clogged with blood clots. Bleeding from around their site or the needles coming loose. These are all things that have to be watched for during treatment, for the patient's safety.

One thing about a dialysis nurse is that you get very close to your patients. Your patient comes in three times a week and stays from 3 to 4 hours or more. The patients have had to change their lives around, trying to find out how to fit these treatments in their lives. They have to decide whether to come in Monday, Wednesday, Friday or Tuesday, Thursday, Saturday and what shift will work for them, and their lives. Coming in at 5:00-5:30 am, 10:00-10:30 am, or 2:30-3:00 pm and staying on for the 3 to 4 or more hours is also taken into consideration. They must figure out how to find transportation in and back home. Getting this to fit with their jobs or finding a job that will work with them is significant. These treatments can last for years. Not all patients are able to get a kidney transplant.

One of my clients had been on dialysis for more than 15yrs when I started, and a few years later he started having to care for his wife that was going through some physical things as she was growing older. So, kidney failure affects one's life and their families in a very big way. The two main problems that can cause kidney failure are Diabetes or High Blood pressure, but they are not the only ones.

When I decided to be a nurse there was one thing I knew for sure, and this was how I would care for my patients. I care for them as I would care for my family. They are either my Mom, Dad, Sister, Brother, or Husband and Children. You are part of my life now and someone I know. I will take care of you as a family member. Not only taking care of the physical but also the emotional side, the feelings - how the patient is dealing with what is going on. Giving them encouragement, positive words, even though one time in nursing school I was told I should never talk about God to my patients. Well God is part of my life and He is the one that helped me get through things in my life so I could become a nurse. If the patient believes I will share, if they want or like scripture verses or prayer I will share. God is much bigger than all of us. Of course, if they don't want it, I will respect that. I am also focusing on the medical part first and help them settle into their treatment.

One gentleman I remember taking care of was just starting his treatment and had a port which is usually placed in the chest.

This poor gentleman had already been through a lot. He did not come to us do to something he had not tried to take care of like diabetes or high blood pressure. He had recently found out he had Cancer. He had lived a life with hardly any problems and now in his later life he finds out this. He had been planning on retiring and traveling around the United States with his wife. Unfortunately, during the process of being diagnosed with Pancreatic Cancer they did a test having to use dye. In this process his body reacted very bad to this dye causing his kidneys to start shutting down. His Physicians thought starting dialysis may help to get his kidneys to heal and start working again. So, the gentleman came to us being aggravated with medical workers, frustrated with where his life was going and knowing he would have to trust other people in the medical field. At this point, he had already lost the trust in them after what he had gone through.

I am a person who sees another individual going through difficult times and asking myself how I would handle this. I am a positive person also so when I answer people's questions or talk to them, I try to keep it upbeat and encouraging. He was terribly angry at this time not only at life and what was going on, but at people. So, he did not talk very nice to people when he did talk. Could you blame him? He had not seen this when he had planned his life and what would happen as he became older.

He was with us for weeks and as time continued, he found out his kidneys would not be coming back. His physicians helped him get on the transplant list, but he would be getting a double transplant both pancreas and kidney which could take a little longer. Anywhere from months to years for it to happen. He would have to continue dialysis and treatment for his cancer. As time went on, we all worked to help him to relax more. I continued to encourage him with positive and kind words when he would look at things in a negative way. He started not being so sharp speaking to the nurses and the technicians, and he would talk to us a little more.

Nursing is not all about the medical part, you touch people's lives in other ways, but they also touch yours. You have to learn to try to leave it all at the job, but it is not always that easy. We are human and it follows us home. I am thankful to have a relationship with God and it is as I rest in Him, I am comforted. He keeps me strong. When working with individuals I am able to share God with them if they want me to. Some people don't but that does not change how I care for them because I am there to help them through this time in as much as a positive way I can. I will tell people to rest in Gods arms when I see they need it. With this patient he had his strong wall up due to all what he had just been through. I could tell he took my positive words and comforting words in, but he did not open up a lot. As he was there longer, he opened up a little more and would talk about things every so often. I would share those comforting words with him and shared a few of Gods words.

One day I came in to work and looked at the list of clients to see who was not coming to be able to call them and check in on them. That was the day we found out that this gentleman was going in for his transplants. He had been called in the night before to come in the hospital for the transplant. We were so excited for him. His transplant went well, he had a few more dialysis treatments in the hospital before his new kidney started working for him. Everyone in the clinic was very happy for him. Maybe five months or so went by, and by then sometimes our patients would come in to visit us with their new kidney.

We did not get to see this gentleman again though. We did get a message by one of his family members that he had gone to see the Father. We all were sad to hear this. We all had known how blessed he had been when he got that call for his transplant, and how happy he had been not to have to come back for treatment. When reading his obituary, they shared in it his love for God, and his thanks for his care during the time he had dialysis. I was very blessed to hear that the words of God I shared probably touched his heart. So, the things we do physically for our patients matter yes, they do, but the things we say matter too. Making that patient feel that having them there in that time matters and we are there for them means a lot. So, I always remind myself as I take care of people that it matters how you treat them just not physically but also emotionally. They are a person and every one of us matters to God.

Christel Roberts / RN / Dialysis Nurse / CNA

BIOGRAPHY: Christel Roberts lives in Douglasville, PA with her husband and family. Christel worked as a CNA (Certified Nursing Assistant) for two years as a single mom before she remarried and was a stay-at-home mom for seven years. After which she went back to school and became a Registered Nurse. Her first full time job as a nurse was as a Dialysis Nurse where she quickly learned that nursing involves being as invested emotionally as well as medically in your patients.

DOMESTIC VIOLENCE

It was an evening shift, from one to nine pm at the hospital where I worked, and about seven pm. Two more hours and I would be handing over report to the night nurse. Then, it happened – what all nurses dread, a call from Emergency Room to give report on a new admission. It was a male surgical floor, so it could be anything, I was hoping it would be a simple surgical case. I answered the phone and my heart sank – it was third-degree burns covering about 90% of his body. The hospital did not have a separate burn unit, so all burns were admitted to the surgical unit. Doctors' orders were to submerge patient in a saline bath and follow with a Silvadene wet dressing. I braced myself and alerted the male nurse that I would need help with this one.

Mr. P was groaning and crying in pain and as we cleaned and dressed him, he told us his wife had doused him in kerosene and lit him on fire. As my nurse colleague got angry and indignant about how wicked his wife was, I just continued to listen intently, then quietly asked, "what happened, what did you do? She did not just decide to do this for nothing, did she?" Well, the nurse was beside himself. "Candie, how could you say that, you think that is ok?" "Absolutely not," I responded but we do not know the full story. As we paused and waited, Mr. P stated he came in from work, they had a fight and that his wife did this when he fell asleep.

As a nurse, no matter what my opinion I always give every patient the best care and attention and this was no different. We settled him for the night, sedated him, I told him I was sorry for his pain and we would do everything we could to help him be as comfortable as possible. He expressed his thanks, and we were soon off duty.

The following day, as I walked in to worked, I met a woman standing at the door to the unit. I asked if I could help her and she replied that she was Mr. P's wife and she was waiting to see him when we opened the doors for visiting hours. I replied that after what she did, I was surprised she was interested in visiting him, but that she would be allowed in after we had changed shifts. She thanked me and started to talk with tears streaming down her face; stating she was praying he would be OK. As I handed her a tissue, I reassured her we were doing everything we could and he would be well cared for, but that the burns were very extensive.

As she kept talking my heart went out to her. It was a tale of domestic physical, verbal and mental abuse that lasted for many years – if I remember correctly, they had been married for about fifteen years. She had endured numerous severe beatings, raped in a drunken rage many times right after coming home announcing he had just had sex with another woman on his way home. There were times he would not even wait for their young children to be asleep and did not care if they were in the same room. It was right after one of these episodes and he would not take no for an answer. She was brutally raped following which he poured hot sauce into her vagina. He had done did previously, but this was the first time he used almost the whole bottle – probably about 12-16 ounces. Being much smaller than him she was unable to fight him off or prevent it.

That was the straw that broke the camel's back. He eventually fell asleep laughing at her as she cried and attempted to wash as much of the hot sauce out. She just knew she could not go on living that way and she had to do something. As she watched him sleeping, she noticed the container of kerosene they used to fill the lantern. She reached for it, and without thinking, started pouring, lit the match and as she saw the flames ignite was aware of what she had just done. He woke with a start and ran out screaming for help and was brought to the ER by a neighbor. She acknowledged that she had done something terrible and was contrite, stating she just didn't know what else to do.

Initially when she was first allowed in to visit Mr. P., he was angry and refused to talk to her. He also had the whole floor and nurses on his side, everyone being sympathetic to his suffering. Mrs. P stood there, humiliated and in tears as verbal assaults were lashed out. When I walked over, there stood a police officer waiting for a statement. I put my arms around

Mrs. P and suggested Mr. P tell the full story, not just his version. He was indignant at first but eventually did and decided not to press charges; even apologizing to his wife. Mr. P remained on our unit for weeks and his wife visited every day, feeding him and praying for him; they left and went back to their home together when he was discharged. This was one of the few cases of domestic violence I have seen resolved in that manner. Mr. P was badly scarred for life, but no one died.

Candia Cumberbatch-Lucenius, MHA / RN-Midwife / BSN / CPHM

HOME HEALTH NURSING

Working as a Home Health Nurse in Baltimore in the mid '90s was a choice I made to transition from the Telemetry or Cardiac Stepdown unit where I had worked for several years. Several of my cases remain in my memory, one being the 88-year-old woman who did not want to relinquish her independence and asked me to convince her children to give her back the keys to her car. My assignment was to visit her at home every other day to administer a high-end soap water enema for chronic constipation and severe impaction. Not as bad as it sounds, which I found out several years later is what they do in those 'hydraulic' cleansing centers. She had everything set up by the time I arrived, so I added the lubricant to the tip and had a pretty sophisticated privacy system set up with screens and a gown. She used the bathroom after resting in place for about half hour.

The other case I can vividly remember is a mother/baby wellness check. Mother was a petite 17-year-old primigravida, and baby was a tiny 6-pound 2-ounce girl. Arriving at the address I had been given, I wondered if I was in the right place. About five or six young men, maybe between 17 and 20, who had been standing around smoking and generally being quite loud, quickly surrounded my car. I gingerly rolled down my window and said a sheepish 'hi', although sounding much braver than I felt at the time. I was greeted with, "you the nurse?" "Yes, I am" I replied. "You here for M and her baby?" another asked. Again, I confirmed. One guy speaking with some authority said, "Come wid me, I'll take you to her." And to his friends "Step aside," which they all did while I followed the leader up three maybe four (I've forgotten now) flights of stairs up a winding fire escape.

When he ushered me into the room and greeted the young mother with "the nurse here," I was slightly taken aback. The 'room' if you can call it that was no bigger than a bathroom. In a corner was piles of boxes and containers overflowing with clothes, and to one side was a twin bed with the baby in the middle surrounded by piles of clothes and pillows. She found a small bowl and heated some water using an electric kettle peeking out from under the piles of everything, and that was what I used to demonstrate giving her baby a bath. We were able to make enough space next to baby for mom's exam.

It was not easy to do, but I tried to help her organize and declutter, instructing her to keep the bed as free of clothes as possible to keep the baby safe and avoid suffocation under the pile. Another nurse did the follow-up visit and I didn't see this young mother again. I think about her and baby off and on and wonder how things turned out for them.

Candia Cumberbatch-Lucenius, MHA/RN-Midwife/BSN/CPHM

WHEN IT'S ONE OF OUR OWN

He was fun, active, had the biggest smile and we became fast friends from the day he joined our hospital staff. We enjoyed working together – he was always so helpful, going out of his way to lend a hand whenever and wherever needed. He was liked by all nurse's male and female and made many friends. One of the things I especially liked about Nurse D was that he was a family man – his girlfriend came first, and he enjoyed talking about her – they were planning to get married soon he shared. "I would love for you to me her Candie" he stated, "you'll like her" he added gushing. A few months later he was beaming from ear to ear, they were postponing the wedding because his girlfriend was pregnant, but it would happen as soon as the baby came. I was happy for him, one couldn't help but be – he was so excited, he was full of life and just an all-around great person.

I was scheduled to do night shift rotation and Nurse D was doing a mental health orientation off campus, so I didn't see him for several weeks. One day I was heading home after my shift and who should I run into but my friend Nurse D. After sharing pleasantries, asking about his girlfriend, baby etc. – he was the proud papa of a handsome baby boy, he stated he had bad news. Puzzled, I just stared at him, nothing he had said sounded like bad news. "Candie," he almost whispered "the doctors think I have cancer." "What?" I responded in disbelief, refusing to accept what I had heard. "Yes" Nurse D replied, "I am actually on my way to see an orthopedic surgeon. They think the best course of action to try and save my life is to do an above knee amputation."

OK, now back it up, how did that happen, when? My questions were flying off my tongue and D had to laugh even facing such a serious diagnosis. He was playing sports and was hit hard on the shin by the ball. He was having pain for several months, but like most men, told himself to "suck it up, it was nothing," until the pain became unbearable, and it looked like there was some underlying infection – the area was hot to touch and swollen. The diagnosis "bone cancer". We hugged and cried, I told him I would be praying for him so he would have the best outcome.

The next time I saw Nurse D, he looked noticeably thinner, even slightly gaunt with a decisive limp, obviously in pain. He just couldn't accept the amputation, couldn't go through with it, but he wasn't getting better, by now the doctors told him, they were sure it had spread. At that point, I was even angry at him. "Nurse D, you're a nurse you know better. When we last spoke, you were on your way for a consult to schedule the surgery. Why wouldn't you do something that might save your life; what about your baby?" He broke down "I know, I don't want to leave my baby, and my girlfriend – I don't know what she'll do without me. I was so stupid putting it off, but I'm

afraid Candie." Reassuring him, I accompanied him to the
surgeon's appointment where he was admitted right away and
scheduled for surgery first thing the following morning. After
the surgery, Nurse D was understandably saddened but
hopeful for a second chance to see his son grow up and marry
his soul mate.

He was out on sick leave for several weeks, then re-admitted
for a second amputation due to non-healing wound thought to
be spread of the cancer. When I cared for him post-op, I
prayed for him, and encouraged him not to give up. He was
excited for me – I was pregnant, and we focused on that for a
while. All the other nurses came around at various times and
shifts to give extra TLC to our co-worker who always brought
joy to everyone and was in the fight of his life.

Fast forward I had just delivered a healthy baby boy and was
on maternity leave when I received a call at about 1am from
another nurse. "Nurse Cumberbatch, Nurse D was just
admitted, he's not doing well, and asking for you. So sorry for
calling this late." I asked to speak to him, explained I just had
my baby one week ago, and couldn't make it in to the hospital,
but I would be praying for him and try to see him in a few
days if I could. That seemed to calm him down for a bit, but
before he hung up, he cried out with such pain and fear,
"Candie, I don't want to die, I don't want to die!" "I know, I'll
be praying for you" and I did pray with him before he calmed

down and fell asleep. It was 5am when I received another call from the hospital, letting me know my friend Nurse D had died – he had lost his fight with the dreaded cancer as he slowly whispered, "Call Candie for please; then tell Candie goodbye, and thanks." We were all crying at this point. It was a sad farewell with nurses from all over coming to say goodbye to one of our own.

Candia Cumberbatch-Lucenius, MHA / RN-Midwife / BSN / CPHM

REWARDS – BETTER THAN MONEY

It's about 10am on a busy Telemetry unit; we've made our rounds and started administering medications. The Nursing Assistants or Technicians are helping patients with breakfast, baths, and making them comfortable. I walk into a room to hang IV fluids and the patient, a 60 plus year old man, post cardiac by-pass, is slouched down in the bed, his feet hanging over the bottom headboard; he is struggling unsuccessfully to prop himself up in the bed.

"Good morning, how are you doing this morning." I greet my patient with a smile. "I'm going to change your IV fluids and give you your medications. Has the nursing assistant been in to check on you?" He replied that she did stop by briefly but was called away to help with someone else. Without hesitation, I laid down everything, walked into the bathroom, got everything together and proceeded to give him a bed bath which I finished off with an "old school" back rub. Those of you who were training initially at a Hospital School of Nursing know exactly what I'm talking about. You start off with a nice soapy lather - using both hands you gently massage the back in a clockwise circular motion, from collar bone down to the lower back. For patients prone to bed sores that would also include the butt cheeks (not necessary in this case). After rinsing off all the suds with a washrag, you change the water as needed, you would follow that with rubbing alcohol, or for

those of us trained and who worked in a Caribbean hospital —
Limacol, Citracol, Bay-rum or Alcolado; and finish off with a
light dusting of baby or talcum powder.

Now, don't get me wrong; we were busy — I'm talking about a
cardiac stepdown unit with a case load of seven to ten patients
each; patients leaving the floor for tests or procedures and/or
returning and new admissions or transfers from the intensive
care unit were a general part of the day. In the back of my
mind, I was thinking about all the other patients and getting
all my work done, including accurate documentation, but my
other thought was 'what if that was my father or brother or
myself' for that matter. Once I was done and had changed the
bed linen, helping my patient get more comfortable in bed,
and propped up on nicely fluffed pillows, I stood back and said
with a smile, "How does that feel?" He looked up at me with
his eyes full of tears and sobbed, "I didn't think nurses like you
still existed." I thanked him and reassured him there were
many more nurses who would be blessed to do the same.

I left that room feeling like I had won one million dollars; that
feeling of satisfaction that I had helped my patient be
comfortable, alleviate his pain and just feel better, was almost
over whelming.

The rest of the day was filled with moving quickly from room
to room, administering medications and pain killers, changing
IV's, getting patients ready and sent to OR for a Cardiac

Catheterization, CABG, Stent or for tests, and receiving them back after the procedure. It was another long day with no lunch break.

And yes, I did have to stay over a little to finish my notes, but it was well worth it; like they say in that advertisement "priceless".

Candia Cumberbatch-Lucenius, MHA / RN-Midwife / BSN / CPHM

A COMMON MALE DIAGNOSIS

Benign Prostatic Hypertrophy was the admitting diagnosis, very common in men over fifty. Also called prostate gland enlargement, symptoms which include feeling the bladder is full all the time and that they have to urinate right away, and often, weak urine flow, having difficulty starting to urinate, and needing to push or strain seem more uncomfortable, annoying and troubling than something to get overly concerned about. The flow of urine is blocked with other urinary tract or kidney problems.

JT was prepped and sent to surgery for a routine TURP (Transurethral resection of the prostate). He returned with the IV fluids in place flowing wide open, an antibiotic IV bag of Vancomycin with orders to administer every twelve hours. The urinary irrigation system set up to keep the urine flowing and to prevent the formation of blood clots, which were extremely painful.

As soon as Mr. S (surgeon) walked in we had a sense it was bad news. He shared that what was supposed to be a simple, routine, common-place procedure turned into a radical resection for a stage 3 cancer with significant spread, assumed to be more stage four but needed the path report to confirm. It was hard to see him go over the operating notes several times before asking me to accompany him to JT's bedside to deliver the devastating news to him and his wife who had waited until after the surgery to see him. Another emotional experience to witness the sadness and agony of such a devastating prognosis. After Mr. S left it was up to me to comfort and reassure them that we would continue to do all we could for as long as we could.

It might have been the shock of the news, or maybe due to the surgery aggravating the cancer, but after we sedated him and his wife left promising to return first thing in the morning, JT died peacefully in his sleep. His wife came, looking dejected and defeated, held his hand finding some comfort in the fact that he would not be in pain. I hugged her, cried and prayed with her and stayed with her until he was removed from the floor. As a nurse who views my profession as a divine calling, I realize that healing has many forms. Not able to nurse JT back to full health, I felt what I was able to offer his wife was a form of healing.

Candia Cumberbatch-Lucenius, MHA / RN–Midwife / BSN / CPHM

MY MIRACLE ON MATERNITY

Throughout my nursing career, I had many memorable experiences, but it is those I had as a midwife that have remained indelible in my mind. I cannot forget my first hospital delivery nor my first home delivery. How can I not remember when, as a community health nurse/midwife, I had to walk a muddy track very late on a rainy night, guided by a flambeau (a local torch), to deliver a mother at home, by the light of a small kerosene lamp! But foremost in my mind is an experience on night duty at Victoria Hospital during my first year as a qualified midwife.

A night on "Maternity" (which was what we called the obstetric ward, at the time) was very unpredictable. The night could start with no patients in active labor and a few empty beds, but that was most likely to change in no time. Very often, by the time you are ready to go off duty the next morning, there would be cots and mattresses on the floor to accommodate the many admissions for the night. Reporting for duty on "Maternity" on a regular night could start with being greeted with moans and groans from mothers in labor. You might even hear them as you disembark the nurses van before you reach the door as "Maternity" was the first ward and the delivery room overlooked the entrance to the hospital. A quick glance around the front part of the ward upon entering the door, would give an indication of what was in store for the night. Cots and mattresses on the floor with women in active labor meant it would be a rough night.

At that time there was a single room with two beds for labor and delivery. The lone infant incubator was at the back in the outer ward. Mothers were delivered by midwives unless it was a specific request by the patient or obstetrician, the patient was at risk or there was some complication during labor.

One memorable night, there would be two of us on duty. My colleague and I had recently graduated as midwives from the same midwifery class. As we entered the ward, it seemed quiet, but we noticed that only the ward sister was at the desk and some cries were coming from the labor room. I realized then that it was not going to be as quiet a night as I first thought. After the usual greeting and pleasantries, we were given a verbal report by the ward sister and did our usual drug and other checks. We went around the ward quickly to greet and check on the patients to ensure that they were comfortable and in no need of immediate care. We then proceeded to relieve the nurses in the labor room.

As we pushed the door open, we saw the look of relief on the faces of the two nurses in there! I could very well understand that feeling. This is a feeling we all experience when we have patients in labor, and we see our relief nurse approaching. Yes, both beds were occupied with women in advanced labor with a midwife attending to each of them. We walked through the door just in time to hear one of the women give that intense grunt and final push, as her baby was delivered. Another sigh of relief by the nurses and the mother!

After a report from the nurses, my colleague quickly took over the care of the woman who had just delivered. The baby was fine and healthy. I went to attend to the other patient, a primigravida who had been in labor for a good while; she was very close to deliver but visibly exhausted. The baby's head was fully crowned and visible, but she complained of being too weak to push. After much encouragement and with just two pushes, the baby boy was finally delivered! But oh! The baby came out pale and "flat", not breathing, not crying even with stimulation! I thought we had lost him! I prayed asking God not to allow that to happen. I quickly wrapped him in a blanket and gave him some oxygen. He gave a gasp. I asked my colleague to attend to the mother and sped out of the labor room with him straight to the incubator where he could get some piped oxygen and warmth. I continued to rub him firmly for more warmth and stimulation. Slowly, I began to see regular movement of his chest, his breathing was becoming normal and the paleness giving way to a healthy pink color. I gave him a firm flick underneath his foot; he responded with a lusty cry! I breathed a sigh of relief! Oh, how I thanked God! He was now quite active, stretching and moving his limbs about. I called him Baby D.

After asking his guardian angel to take care of him, I quickly went back to attend to his mother who, thankfully was in no distress. My colleague had taken over her care so I could attend to the baby emergency. The mother was genuinely concerned about the baby and I reassured her that he had given a very hearty cry and was doing well. I sutured her episiotomy, cleaned her up, made her comfortable and took her to her bed. Since the baby was now doing fine, I took him to her so she could hold him for a while. I later brought him back to the incubator where he would spend the rest of the night, as a precaution. Throughout the night, I kept checking on him to make sure he was okay.

After my colleague and I settled the two mothers comfortably, we then checked on the other patients and sat down to write our reports. No sooner had we completed this task, we heard the door open and…yes, an admission! Thankfully, she was not in active labor. My colleague went to attend to her. Whilst she was in the labor room completing the examination of the mother who had just been admitted, another admission walked in. We continued having admissions until the three empty beds were filled and three cots had to be put down to accommodate the others. That kept us on our feet the whole night, with barely enough time to attend to the other patients and write our reports. We were grateful that up to this time there were no emergencies or anyone who came in ready to deliver.

About half an hour before the scheduled time to go off duty, we heard a commotion. It was a woman coming through the door walking with her legs wide apart and screaming that she was ready to deliver. Since all beds were taken and the lone labor/delivery room was occupied with women who were being examined, I quickly got up and put one of the spare mattresses on the floor so she could lie on it. Yes, she was fully dilated, and the baby's head was very visible. I only had time to put on a pair of gloves before she gave a vigorous push and the baby was delivered. She came out quite active, waving and greeting the world with a very energetic cry. By that time, the labor room had become empty, so I brought the mother in to continue her care.

While attending to her, I looked up and could see a nurse through the little glass panel at the top of the door of the labor room. Oh! What a pleasant sight! What a relief to see the day staff! I gave a verbal report to the relief nurse and handed the patient over to her. By that time, my colleague had given the night's report to the day staff. I greeted them, wrote my case report and was soon on my way home.

What a night! That was not an atypical night though; it was almost a regular night on "Maternity".

At that time, a primigravida who had a normal delivery was kept in hospital for two days. There being no problems with neither baby D nor mother, they were discharged from hospital.

Many years later, a lady stopped me while I was at the local market and greeted me quite happily, "Nurse, nurse, that's your boy! I looked at her somewhat perplexed. She must have seen the expression on my face because she continued, "You don't remember us, nurse?" I sheepishly answered "Nooooo, remind me", as I realized that she was all excited and wanted me to meet her boy. It was then she told me that he was Baby D! How happy I was to see this healthy, tall, and handsome seventeen-year old young man! The mother admitted then, how scared she was during labor that unforgettable night, and how she thought she had lost the baby when he didn't cry at birth and when she saw me ran out of the labor room with him.

It felt so rewarding and I felt so blessed to know that I had been a part of what I considered a miracle! I thank God again for coming through for me and for them that night. Every time I see this young man or his mother, I remember my miracle on "Maternity".

Bernadette Springer, RN/Midwife/Community Health Nurse/
Women Affairs Officer/Health Clinic Administrator

BIOGRAPHY: Bernadette Springer was born in Castries, Saint Lucia and spent most of her childhood and young-adult years living in the village of Gros-Islet.

Upon graduation from St Joseph's Convent Secondary school,

Bernadette entered the Victoria Hospital School of Nursing in 1976 and graduated as a Registered Nurse in 1979. She went on to become a certified midwife in 1981. For about twelve years she served diligently as a Staff Nurse/Midwife at Victoria Hospital and later as a Community Health Nurse.

Bernadette took a break from Nursing and joined the Civil Service as Women's Affairs Officer in the Division of Women's Affairs (presently the Division of Gender Relations). The thirteen years spent in that position, allowed her the privilege of travelling throughout Saint Lucia continuing her interaction with the community.

In 2001 she went back into the field of health and became the first Administrator of the newly established Gros-Islet Polyclinic, a post she held until 2006 when she took early retirement to relocate to the United States of America to join her husband.

Bernadette Springer is married to Cletus Springer and they are blessed with a beautiful and loving daughter, Cleisha-Bernise.

20TH CENTURY EPIDEMIC
HIV / AIDS

In 1980, the talk about a new virus identified as the Human Immunodeficiency Virus (HIV) reared its ugly head. It was found that there were a few isolated cases as far back as 1960, but they went basically unnoticed or ignored until about 1981 when it seemed to flare up in California. It manifested itself by clusters of Kaposi's sarcoma and pneumocystis pneumonia in gay men living in Los Angeles and New York. That's when the world started to take notice and it was first reported. What is HIV? It is a virus that attacks the CD4 cells (or T cells) of the immune system. The mode of transmission is through bodily fluids such as blood, semen, vaginal fluids, anal fluids, and breast milk; and most been spread through unprotected sex, drug users sharing of needles and birth.

As it spreads over time so many CD4 cells are destroyed, and the immune system is so compromised that the body cannot fight off any infections or diseases and that eventually leads to the most severe form of the HIV infection: acquired immunodeficiency syndrome (AIDS). When AIDS develops the person is very susceptible to cancer and other life-threatening infections, such as pneumonia. It took several years, and after about more than 70 million people infected with HIV and about 35 million have died from AIDS according to the World Health Organization (WHO), people treated with an anti-viral drug that halts it's spread, can live with the infection for years.

I was working a twelve-hour night shift on a Telemetry floor in Baltimore probably mid-1992. It was about two am when I was told I was getting an emergency room admission, diagnosis AIDS. Up to that time, I had not personally had direct contact with an HIV positive patient. We had several in the hospital of course and I had assisted on the floor with the other patients while the nurse took care of her assigned patient. But after several years of the HIV/AIDS pandemic, I was not comfortable admitting the patient. Soon after I took report from the ER nurse, the stretcher was wheeled down the hallway and I quickly moved ahead to make sure I had covered everything, and the room was ready.

Two doctors - the attending and the resident, one ER nurse, one IV nurse and the respiratory therapist all accompanied the patient. He had recently been bagged and a breathing tube placed before he was brought up to my floor. As were most patients diagnosed with HIV/AIDS then, he was DNI/DNR. I was slightly taken aback when I moved closer to assist in getting him from stretcher to bed. He was about 6 feet 5 inches, light skin toned, wavy black hair and one of the most handsome men I've ever seen. Single at the time, my first thought was "damn he's good looking! What a waste."

As we settled him making him as comfortable as possible, the attending informed me that every one of them had tried and were not able to start an IV; he had found a vein, but it blew. He definitely needed the fluids though – with a temperature of 105 degrees Fahrenheit he was literally burning up. After carefully assessing him all over I was able to find a small vein on his foot near the ankle. Using a butterfly, we were able to draw his blood and then start an IV of Lactate Ringers wide open. Next, I washed him down with cold water, and changed his clothes and bed linen, still thinking what a gorgeous hunk of male masculinity he was. And his eyes when he looked up to ask for some ice chips – boy in his day he must have been something. (Don't judge me – he was really good looking). I also thought that he must be gay because how else would he end up with that diagnosis. For several years after it began to spread, HIV/AIDS was considered a gay man's disease. It was sometime before the world realized that it was not confined to just that population.

I spend the next 2 hours changing his IV, washing him to keep his temperature down; it never went below 104. He slept briefly off and on once we administered IV Demerol and woke up just to ask for ice chips, which we kept at his bedside. He died peacefully about five am, we said our final goodbye after we had prepped him for the morgue, and the resident had informed the family. No tears this time, but we were all truly sad.

Candia Cumberbatch-Lucenius, MHA/RN-Midwife/BSN/CPHM

MS. FAY

Tuesday morning. Usually the busiest day of the week on a Med Surg/Oncology Unit, I braced my mind and body for a real "work-workout". I had been off for the weekend and Monday and did not know "what" was in store for me. I put my lunch and handbag away and was ready for report. Boy, did I get an ear full!! It was all ...mostly about one patient. "She was the worst", they kept saying. Guess what? She is assigned to Kathleen. "you are in for a treat, one nurse sarcastically said."

For privacy purposes, my patient's name is Fay. Report was long, and I had seven patient's that day. This was both a good and bad thing. Good because, I would not get the first or second admission, and bad cause, I had 2 blood transfusions and one chemo admission. PLUS, the supposedly "difficult patient".

I made my rounds and decided to make Fay my last stop as I wasn't sure "what" the issue with her was, and I did want to at least see my other patients and greet them before the busy day took off.

I got held up with a few little requests from my other patient's such as "pull me up in bed, please," and an IV antibiotic was completed and the pump was beeping, so I had to flush that one , etc... So, it took a lot longer to get to Fay's room, than I anticipated. Some other requests, I called my CNA to carry out and finally made it to Fay's room.

"Good morning, Ms. Fay, my name is Kathleen. I am going to be your nurse today. How was your night? We are at shift change, so is there anything I can get you, that you need right away?"

FAY > "Took you long enough! Are you an RN or an aide.?"

Me > "I am a registered nurse."

Fay > "Then get out of my room and get me the aide."

Me > "Anything the aide does for you, I can do, Ms. Fay. I would be happy to help you."

Fay > "Girl, my bed has not been changed since Saturday, I'm hungry cause, I did not like what they were giving out for dinner, I need to shower, and change into a CLEAN" (yelling) "night gown, my water jug has not been changed since yesterday. I want to sit in the chair for a while but can't get the hell out of this cage they put me in." (referring to the bed with the side rails up)

I realized at that point that it would take every ounce of patience, that I had to deal with this patient and still be courteous, and helpful. So, I stood listening and writing down everything she said.

FAY > "ARE YOU A DAMN SECRETARY"?

Me > "No Ms. Fay. I understand, however, because I have 6 other patients. I want to make sure, I get it right and get you all what you ask for, so you do not feel neglected."

Fay > "Hmm!! That's a first. You all come in here and run out so quick, and never listen to what I ask for, so I am ALREADY neglected."

In my mind.... I said... "No sh....! Who wants to listen to THAT all day? We are here to help her not be her slave!"

But out loud, I said "Maybe I work a little differently, Ms. Fay; so please help me out here and let's work together."

Fay > "TOGETHER?? Are we going to spend your paycheck TOGETHER?"

Ok, say what you will, but this one was funny, so I smiled. That did not go over well

Fay > "YES, laugh at me! You BI..."

Me > "I am not laughing at you, Ms. Fay, that was a funny saying, admit it".

Finally, after this went on for a while, I started cleaning up her room, I helped her out of bed, I helped her with her shower, etc and etc and etc. When I was done and all her "requests" were taken care of., we had her diet discussion and came up with a compromise. I was finally ready to go start on my other patient's and heard another IV beeping which meant the first pint of blood on MR T was completed. I explained to Fay what my next couple hours would be like with the blood and the chemo and that any chance I got, in between, I would come back to check on her.

Fay >"Yeh, Yeh, Yeh! As usual, I will see you tomorrow morning with an excuse as to you being too busy to come back. I know the drill."

Me > "No, Fay. I will see you in a short bit."

Fay grunted something under her breath, and off I went. Blood went up, first 2 fifteen minutes check done, Patient said he felt fine. Called Nurse S to check the chemo with me for accuracy. Then hung the drug after explaining about the drug and the side effects and what signs and symptoms to report. Made my way to patient 4, 5 6 and seen and unfortunately, Patient 7 wants to leave AMA. He did not want to listen to anything or talk to anyone. He had a really bad night and wanted OUT. After calling his physician, he signed his AMA paper and walked out. (some patients do that when they KNOW that they were not really sick in the first place).

By then it was about 12noon. I checked on my chemo guy and the blood transfusion patient and true to my word went back to see Fay.

Fay > "Well what do you know? Put me back to bed and get my lunch."

I complied.

This went on with Ms. Fay throughout this shift. At the end of the shift. I made it a point to go to her room to say good night and that I would see her in the morning. She was reading, and shouted "Why are you disturbing my sleep, girl? I chose not to point out that she was reading, apologized and closed her door softly.

Now I am NOT a pushover by any means necessary, but I loved challenges, and this was one I WAS going to conquer. I remembered an old saying my mom used to say " you will never catch flies with vinegar, spread some honey, and you get more than you ask for" so, that became my plan. The next few workdays seemed impossible with Ms. Fay. She was really IMPOSSIBLE!! I prayed and even cried a time or 2 and still Ms. Fay seemed like she would not let up. But I had accepted the challenge, so I wasn't going to let up either. I read through Ms. Fay's chart several times, reading her social history over and over again, and finally, something jumped out at me. We are now on Day 4 of my workdays; I would be working till Saturday and would be off Sunday and Monday.

Saturday morning came and I first took Ms. Fay's chart to read one more time. This lady was scared. She was all alone, her husband left her, when she was diagnosed with ovarian cancer, and she never had any kids. She did not grow up in this area and had not made any friends here. She was the principal of a high school and REALLY knew how to "make people listen to her."

This Saturday morning. I went to Ms. Fay's room first. There were no blood transfusions or chemo waiting. So, my opening statement was "Good morning Ms. Fay. How are you feeling?" No answer.

I continued "after today I will be off for 2 days, so I will be hoping things work out and you get to go home. If that happens then I guess you will be a lot more comfortable at home and not have so many people in and out of your room. She pressed the button to raise the head of the bed and looked at me, stared for a while and began to cry. She cried long and hard and I thought she was going to be inconsolable. I walked over to her bed and put my arm around her. I'm sorry if I offended you, I said, I did not mean to.

Fay > "No you did not, and stop calling me Ms. My name is Fay!

Then she told me what I already knew. Her final results came back, and her cancer was spreading; she had, according to the oncologists, a maximum of 3 weeks to live.

FAY > "I have not LIVED! I was robbed of my life. I lost everything, I never had kids, the husband was a jerk and couldn't handle a little nausea and vomiting. God threw me away."

Me > "No He didn't Ms. Fay.... Fay (cause I got "a Look") God's plan for each of us is different. I cannot give you answers for you from Him, but I know, he is not throwing you away."

Fay > "When I first came in as an inpatient, everyone was so high and mighty, treating me like I was an uneducated fool."

Then she proceeded to tell me her life's history, her degrees she acquired, and her status in the community. I told her how proud I felt speaking to such an intelligent person. She thanked me!

The end of shift came quicker than I even expected. So, I went to say good night to my "Real Treat".

She looked weak and exhausted, but alert, and crying again. "Please do not leave she said, I have more money than I need I will pay you! No one else gives a damn. You are the only one who took time to really listen and take care of me."

I apologized and explained that I did have a family and could not stay overnight, but I would see her on Tuesday. Little did I know to what lengths she would go to get what she felt she needed. Early Sunday morning, while drinking my coffee and thanking God for my day off .... finally. My phone rang – it was my Director of nursing, begging me to come in for this lady's sake, she refuses to speak to or let anyone else do anything for her. She specifically wanted "Kathleen, the island nurse". HOW could I say no? I took a shower and did another 14-hour shift. Ms. Fay slept most of the day and I was wondering "what am I doing here? I could have been in my bed too."

This shift was particularly busier than my previous 5 nights and so I stayed longer past 7:30 pm to wrap things up. My plan was to sneak out as I was sure Ms. Fay.... Fay was knocked out........I would be so lucky. Her call light went on, so I reluctantly went to her room. She thanked me for coming in on my day off and handed me an envelope. Me thinking it was money, started to protest. She said, "please do me this last favor. I am sure I won't be asking for anymore. You are the best; God Bless you. These other nurses here should really be more like you...... they are all jokers, every single one of them. "I hugged her and walked out of her room after tucking her blanket around her like she liked. I won't even answer any of the phones, cell or house, I told myself. I will see Fay on Wednesday. The following morning, I woke up, grabbed the envelope and went downstairs to get my favorite elixir, COFFEE! Ok, what is she giving me here? I asked. There were three letters in there one addressed to "my dear loving, jackass of a husband" and two others. One to me, and another to "a girl's name"

I opened mine and read. She asked me to mail the letters to the addresses at the end of my letter. She thanked me excessively and hoped to see me on Wednesday, but highly doubted it, as she said, "My body feels too tired for words. I am really ready to leave this place. I have more peace now than I have had in the 5 years, since this cancer visited me. I know it is because, God did not want to keep me here on earth so he sent me an angel… YOU to make sure I found my way to him in the right frame of mind".

There are stamps in the envelope, and the addresses on the end of this note to you. You know which one is for "the husband". The other one is….and I am sorry I lied to you, is for my daughter. Since my diagnosis, she has not visited or called. I called her once and she answered the phone, telling me that the world did not revolve around me. I prayed and I am still praying for her. But I know as of now it is not doing her no good. However please mail these too letters for me. Again, I am sincerely hoping to see you on Wednesday.

She ended the letter with

"Graciously" Fay

I cried and prayed again, for her, her husband and her daughter.

I got no more calls from the hospital to work extra. I went in to work on Wednesday morning, went straight to Fay's room even before putting my bags away and before getting report. Her room was spotless, the bed was made, there were no IVF fluids hanging, No one laying in the bed............

"Bon voyage, Ms. Fay, I whispered, and walked out to the front desk. Everyone was quiet.

Kathleen Cumberbatch RN/CM/UR Manager

EIGHTEEN YEARS OLD….
…. FORTY EIGHT YEARS OLD

I spent quite a few years working on an oncology floor. The most educated experiences I ever had. I worked extra shifts, because I loved my job.

I was raising four boys, two were my biological ones, one my husband's, before we got hitched and one who self-adopted, because his mom literally did not care where he lived, ate, or slept. He was my older son's friend from high school, and he was well mannered. I did not mind. He got treated like my other 3 sons and got chores assigned too. Most people who have met me get an impression, that I am a B…. < but think on that…. If I were his mom would be in prison now for child neglect. That is a story for a different chapter.

I worked at one of the most renowned hospitals in Baltimore Maryland at the time. One day, I walked on to my floor early (as usual), and surprisingly, my manager was also at work.

"Good morning," I chimed, "was your mattress lumpy and uncomfortable this morning?" I asked her. She smiled. "I wanted to speak with you, before the floor got too busy," she said.

What'd I do now?" I responded. "Come into my office," she said. I followed her. "Should I shut the door? I asked. "Please" she replied.

She started off with "I want to thank you for always being a great example to the team and a good worker. I want to offer you a promotion and I really cannot accept no for an answer.... Please??"

"Does it come with a pay raise?" I asked. "Of course," she replied.

"Then I accept.... wait... what is the promotion about, are you leaving?"

"No", she replied. "I have discussed this with the director, and we want you to be the charge nurse of the unit. I will be the one training you. You will start today, and I will announce it during rounds this morning. Are you ok with that?" "Sure, I said. Let's get started."

I put my lunch away and went into the Lounge room for report and rounds. The announcement was made, and so on and so on.

Rounds and report were almost over. A loud voice was heard saying "ALL NURSES ON STRIKE? WHERE IS EVERYONE?" The manager went out first. The nurses followed. It was a gentleman about 6 foot 1 not too skinny and well dressed. "THERE THEY ARE," He boomed. "I was asked to report to this floor for some alcohol infusion......I mean Chemotherapy" he laughed. This was Forty-eight. Stage 4 advanced lung cancer didn't look it one single bit. "I am afraid to sleep alone so I would like a room close to the nurses' station" he said. We all laughed. The room he got was 3 rooms down from the nurse's station. He was not happy but did not complain. My training began. Making the assignment, and reading charts, then rounds with each doctor who came up. During rounds I got to meet Forty-eight several times. He really was a joyous and lighthearted individual. Throughout the day he would walk the halls and stop and chat about anything to anyone who would listen. As the days went on, he learnt to come to the nurses' station, when his IV Pump started beeping, to either have a nurse flush it or restart it.

One day, 9 days post admit and POD 7 of chemo, he did not come to the desk all day. The nurse assigned to him, reported that he said he "just did not feel right. He was unusually tired, and it just doesn't feel right." We placed a call to his oncologist who asked to do STAT CBC and Chem 7. To our dismay, his platelets came back 3000 (three thousand) I placed a call back to the oncologist who ordered Platelet and FFP (fresh frozen plasma) and 2 units PRBCs. After the first unit of blood was completed, here comes Forty-eight with the empty blood bag, walking to the nurses' station. "I feel like a million bucks," he boomed! "Isn't it faster if I just drink the blood?" We all laughed because we know he was kidding. His nurse led him back to his room to explain to him that he was also neutropenic and needed to stay in his room for a few days away from others, so he won't get an infection at this critical time. Forty-eight was not having it.

"I am having the time of my life, he said. I am spending my sick days with gorgeous women.... I mean nurses, and you want to isolate me? If I wanted to be in prison, I would kill the person that invented cancer." Laughter again. "Listen" he said, " I am a grown man and a well-educated one at that, I know my risks, I read all about this stupid disease when I was diagnosed, but continued to smoke as I was in denial. I was supposed to have started this chemo thing 3 years ago, but I was stubborn. Now, I know my chances of survival are slim to none, but I chose to try.... better late than never, right?" We all smiled but did not respond.

The elevator doors opened, and an older man and wife walked out, but the doors did not close. We could see someone's hand holding it as it tried to close. The man walked back to the elevator and after much whispered persuasion a young girl walked out limping. I thought she was about sixteen or seventeen.

"Good morning, how may I help?" I asked the man who walked up to the desk.

"The doctor asked us to come to this floor, my daughter is to be admitted" he said.

Forty-eight was still standing around and said "Ok, I'm going to take a nap, and will see you ladies after." He walked back to his room accompanied by his assigned nurse. His second unit of blood needed to be started to.

I escorted Eighteen to her room, (found out she was eighteen and had just graduated from high school) and to get her history and start her admission process. I was a bit saddened as I had not seen the admission order and didn't know why she was here. I went to the desk and to my dismay, I read her chart stating that she was here for a possible amputation of that leg. She was diagnosed with bone cancer, and the plan was amputation and then chemo. I took a deep breath and wondered why she was not told. The parents were in the room with her, so I stood up to go call them to another room to speak with them. The elevator door opened up and a young boy, looked to be about EIGHTEEN'S age walked off the elevator and came straight to me. Wanted to know where Eighteen was, he was her boyfriend. I walked him to her room and asked the parents to come sign some papers with me. As soon as they walked out the room, the mother burst into tears, and the father followed suit. I now knew that they knew. But did EIGHTEEN? According to the parents, they asked the doctor to hold off telling her until after the surgery. They were hoping there was a possibility that after he went in, that maybe, just maybe, they could save her leg. She is eighteen, you know, I told them, she is capable of making her own decisions." "We know," they replied, but her life has just begun, we are just not ready to start losing her one piece at a time.

Just at that point the boyfriend came out looking distraught. "She won't let me see the bite on her leg" he complained. "Not today" her father told him, "give her some time." "Ok," he said, but I'm going to have to leave, so I will tell her bye and will come back after the surgery tomorrow.

Since I was going to be the charge nurse, I decided to work a couple night shifts so I had a general picture of how to handle the floor, from both day and night perspective. I left work at 5pm that day with both these cases weighing on my mind. The following day was Eighteen's surgery and I came in to work that night. Forty-eight was doing ok status post all his transfusions and walking around spreading laughter.

I went to Eighteen's room. The scene was heart wrenching. Dad and mom were on either side of her bed crying. Eighteen was having a panic attack, complaining of chest pain and headache. I called her oncologist. He came up with the surgeon. Her surgery ended up with an above the knee amputation and was still bleeding profusely. She was sedated and, I assigned a one to one sitter, in case she woke up. The doctor's left. The parent's stayed. She slept through the night, and at 06:15 AM, I heard the screaming. The sitter could not calm her down. Then as if it could not get any worse the boyfriend showed up, asking questions. He walked into the room and she stretched out both hands to him; he hugged her, and she calmed down some, still crying. Then she screamed "THEY CUT MY LEG OFF!"

"WHAT," he said, "Wait, WHAT??? She then pulled back her covers to show him the reinforced dressed stump. He gagged a few times and said, "no no no nooooooo!" He ran out of the room with her calling after him to come back. He did not. EVER.......

Days went by with Eighteen going into depression and Forty-eight getting stronger, looking forward to discharge. Forty-eight was discharged home 4 days later.

We all missed him but started to focus most of our attention on Eighteen; we took care of the other patients appropriately, and since I was charge, I spent a lot of time in her room. Her parents took turns sleeping over. 10 days post op. Surgeon came to evaluate, along with oncologist. Eighteen was taken for a PET scan. The cancer had spread to her hip and pelvis. No more surgery. Palliative chemo. Eighteen was told the news. This time she didn't cry. She was concerned that her boyfriend never came back and would not answer her texts and calls. She withdrew from everyone including her parents. She refused to eat and did not give consent for a feeding tube. She accepted the chemo and chips of ice, but she became weaker and weaker. The cancer was not kind to this young girl and finally claimed her for its own. I have always wondered, how the parents are doing.

10 weeks after Eighteen departed this earth, Forty-eight comes sauntering on to the floor. I was so glad to see him and looked forward to his snide joking remarks and laughter. He looked tired but was very jovial and acted lively. This admission, went much like the last and he stayed got chemo, got transfused and discharged. I was beginning to think there was light at the end of the tunnel for him. Maybe a happier ending to lift our broken spirit status post EIGHTEEN.

Forty-eight did not return to the hospital for almost 6 months. One freezing cold Sunday morning, Forty-eight came off the elevator, dressed in a pair of jeans, a pair of sandals and a T shirt. I ran to get a blanket and asked to get a few more. We wrapped him up and called for a heating blanket. He lay on the bed shivering even with the heated blanket on. We took turns going in and out and checking up on him. We cranked up the heat in his room and kept a close eye. His oncologist called and we learnt that he was seen in the office 5 days prior and blood work was done. His platelets were seven (seven thousand). He was asked to go for a direct admit. He did not; instead went drinking and drank for 5 days straight. He had to have a central line placed and transfused with platelets, blood, and fluids. This time his platelets were not bouncing back. The more platelets we gave the more they dropped out of sight.

One early morning about 08:30, Forty-eight came walking down the hall with his IV pole, he looked a royal mess, but we were so happy to see him walking. However, knowing his condition I quickly got a wheelchair and had him sit down. He was jovial but to a very small extent. He wanted Tylenol for a headache. I convinced him to allow me and his assigned nurse to wheel him back to his room. He agreed. He was however very restless. He would sit up then stand up then lay down. I knew something was happening internally, but I did not know what. So I asked his nurse to go call his doctor, and to call a code simultaneously. The nurse walked out of the room. Code called. Doctor arrived, Crash cart on standby. He was sedated. So, we walked out to let him sleep it off.

Hours later, here comes recently sedated Forty-eight, asking for something to eat. I walked him back to his room and watched him fall right back asleep, and I promised him I would order his food myself. He was asleep so I went to the desk and ordered him a lunch. The kitchen staff said, they were on the way to deliver lunch so will be there soon. I sat down and started charting. I completed my charting and took to working on the nursing assignments. Nurses were congregating at the desk and getting ready to do some charting of their own. We heard the LOUDEST crash, and we all ran to Forty-eight's room. He was laying on the floor with blood everywhere, Everywhere. We quickly gowned up and made our way to him. He opened his eyes.... And I swear I saw him smile a little and try to speak. I asked him to please just lay still for me. He answered "Yup", and 2 seconds later vomited large amounts of dark red blood. Code team arrived, picked him up placed him on the bed, and Doctors came in took one look and called it. He was gone...

I recall this incident with so much sadness, and confusion. Forty-eight was such a cool dude..

Kathleen Cumberbatch RN/CM/UR Manager

SUCCESSFUL DELIVERY "GRAVEYARD SHIFT"

It was the Summer of 1985 at Sunny Medical Center where I worked the "Graveyard Shift".

The bewitching hours came up that is the time from 2am to 4 am when all hell broke loose.

The Doctors had to run to the Operating Theater for an Emergency Caesarian Section.

The Triage Area was hopping. I was assigned the second admission for the night. She was a

29 yr. old Gravida 3 Para 2 with a history of a previous Caesarian Section 2 years ago. I heard her making grunting and bearing down noises. I quickly got her changed into a gown and on the delivery bed.

On vaginal examination she was fully dilated. This baby had no intension of waiting. I flipped her over to her left side and proceeded with the delivery. I explained to her that her left side was the best option for a good delivery, had her take some deep cleansing breaths, and taught her how to pant. Three short breaths and one long breath to prevent her from pushing the baby out too rapidly. The baby's head gently emerged from the vagina. I checked for the presence of an umbilical cord - not present. I proceeded to deliver the baby to the mother's delight the baby was placed over her abdomen. Her husband assisted in cutting the umbilical cord. The baby weighed 7lbs

5oz with an intact perineum.

One of the doctor's was then free to check the patient and ensure the perineum was intact, and then put her stamp of approval. She then asked how I did it I told her there was something called technique.

Cleo Charles-Philips, RN

WHEN THE NURSE TEACHES THE RESIDENT

Dr. P is a first year Resident in OB who had a delivery that I assisted him with. The patient had a second-degree laceration. DR. P was unsure of the technique to repair the laceration. He approached his Senior resident to ask for advice, and rather than coming to his assistance the senior berated him instead.

Dr. P embarrassed, went on to repair the perineum on his own, which was misaligned and would cause major problems for the patient if it had healed that way. I pointed it out to him and let him know that he would have to undo the repair that he did and do it over. I also informed him I would guide him step by step with the procedure. He listened and this time was successful with a proper alignment. He expressed his gratitude

I informed him it was for the patient's benefit to prevent her from developing complications at a later date.

Cleo Charles-Philips, RN/Midwife

BIOGRAPHY: Cleo Charles-Philips is a Registered Nurse/Midwife from St. Lucia. She has lived and worked in Brooklyn NY for the past 36 years on Labour and Delivery and Maternal/Child to include Anti partum Postpartum NICU and Peds. She is also a Colon Therapist in the Holistic field and is now a Retiree where she continues counseling women and children in her community. She resides in Brooklyn NY with her husband and adult son.

RACISM IN THE WORKPLACE

Once as a nurse in Wilmington Hospital, Dr. K, a black physician from an African country, needed a nurse to assist him with a procedure and also needed an RN to discuss orders. Months previously the hospital instituted a policy where nurses were to wear blue and white scrubs and nursing assistants wore green. In addition to that, nurses had a large, RN badge so that patients can distinguish who the licensed staff was.

Dr. K had gone to the nurse station seeking assistance. At the station was myself, as well as two RNs of Jamaican descent. There was also a blond, older nurse's aide in the vicinity. This doctor, rose from his chair, went directly to the nurse aid to ask her to assist with the procedure as well as process orders.

We explained to the physician that she was the nursing assistant, and we were the RNs. He offered no apologies for his mistake. It made me think that the racism that the larger society has bestowed on us, had affected the thoughts and beliefs even among us. This saddened me to think, that because we were black, this doctor, who probably faced the same discrimination in one way or another, projected that on us.

Also, at Wilmington Hospital, I had gone into the room to check the vital signs of an elderly black woman. Her daughter was in the room. I had my nursing uniform on as well as my large badge indicating myself as an RN. After I had taken the vitals, the patient's daughter asked, "when will the nurse be coming in to see my mother?"

I looked down at my badge, and she apologized for her error. But this goes to show how racism affects us as a people in whole. Not only have some blacks in this country bought into the low expectations that white society often places on us, but even some of us have bought into this belief as well.

Rachel Meister, RN

THE C. DIFF BATTLE

The night nurse finished up her report and I headed down the hall to look in on my patients. I was already dreading it – even before I got there the smell floated out to greet me in the hallway. "Better you than me," snickered Nurse Y, as she rushed past me to do her rounds. I stopped at the door to pull my mask over my face before I peeped in to say good morning and introduce myself to JB, an eighty-five-year-old veteran.

JB was the classic long-term care resident who had been started on antibiotics for an infection. After being on antibiotics for a while, he developed a Clostridium difficile infection or C. Diff as it is known in the medical field. It started with complaints of abdominal pain, bloating and then severe diarrhea. As we know, antibiotics destroy the "good' bacteria in the gut while it's working on killing the infection.

JB had been isolated and felt alone and stigmatized. Isolation meant the signs on the door, and nurses donning mask, gloves and gowns before entering the room to administer medications. He was also very conscious of the strong smell that accompanied every bout of diarrhea. As hard as we tried to maintain strict isolation protocols, in about twenty-four hours 6 other patients on that end of the unit tested positive for C. Diff. We knew the C. Diff spores could have been transmitted by BP cuffs, meal trays, call buttons or even stethoscopes, and were determined to do everything we could to contain it.

We needed to do more – starting with vigorous, consistent and thorough hand-washing with soap and water which is the most effective method to prevent further spread. I reassured JB and the other patients that they would be fine and reached out to the doctor to change the medication to Flagyl (Metronidazole) useful for specific conditions such as anaerobic bacteria and parasites like trichomoniasis, and in the treatment of Helicobacter pylori, (H. pylori) a bacterial infection that causes stomach or intestinal ulcers. All staff were mandated to wear PPE (personal, protective, equipment – gowns, caps, facial masks, and shoe coverings) for contact precautions. Disinfecting surfaces with bleach and other strong disinfectants at the end of every shift proved effective in containing the spread.

Just before JB was discharged, he was started on probiotics (lactobacillus acidophilus), to promote the growth of good bacteria in the gut. Then he was ready to go home and I instructed his family to designate one bathroom that only JB would use. Also, they were encouraged to make sure he is given active yogurt daily – one great source of probiotics. When JB was finally officially discharged, he was at the point where he was not likely to pass on those C. Diff spores but was instructed to keep up the precautions to make sure it stayed that way.

Candia Cumberbatch-Lucenius, MHA/RN-Midwife/BSN/CPHM

POST PARTUM DEPRESSION

Post-Partum Depression is a real thing; it is an actual diagnosis. Most recently known as peripartum depression, it is a form of depression that surfaces gradually during pregnancy and escalates after the delivery. For the majority of pregnant women having a baby is an exciting event, and they along with family are excited about going shopping, having a baby shower, and preparing the nursery.

There are some, and as I found out, a lot more than we think who barely make it thought he pregnancy without a breakdown. Some of the reasons may be financial burdens, wondering how they will support the baby, pay their deductible or in some cases pay the obstetrician and the hospital bill. In other cases, the pregnant woman may be depressed because of marital problems, for example a cheating husband, or maybe just one that is emotionally detached and not sensitive to her needs.

Post-partum or peripartum depression went undetected and undiagnosed for many years, and even when it was recognized it was not taken very seriously. These women suffer silently and painfully with no help and it is surprising some of them even make it through the pain.

She was twenty-something, pretty and smart; great sense of humor and this was her second pregnancy – twins she was told. Her depression started very early on in her pregnancy due to having a toddler already and being a single mother. Pressured by his family, her boyfriend decided he could not be sure the baby was his and walked away stating he would wait to see the baby to decide.

Heart-broken because she was so in love with him, she was no longer her happy, funny self but retreated into a shell of sadness, with hardly an occasional smile. Feeling alone and isolated, she felt like she could not turn to her family. She became indifferent, sullen and only ate small bites becoming very thin and dehydrated. This caused her to have kidney problems during her third trimester leading to some difficulty for her twins after they were born. Her mixed emotions went from excited and being happy to sadness and crying. To top it off, due to the midwife's negligence both baby boys died in the incubator in the NICU.

The young lady was grieving that loss all by herself and she seemed to be spiraling deeper and deeper into depression. As soon as I found out what had happened, I got in touch with her planning to get her out of the house and taking care of herself and little girl. During this time, her daughter lived with the young lady's mother since she was in no condition to take care of her. It was like fighting a losing battle initially, since she just wanted to be left alone, but I refused to take no for an answer. I literally had to get her into the shower, dressed, and after which I styled her hair very nicely getting her to start taking an interest in her looks. We sat together quietly and when I started talking, she listened. After about a week or so, she gradually opened up and with many tears talked about everything that happened. We cried together as I consoled her and prayed with her. Slowly, she agreed to go clothes shopping with me which proved very therapeutic for both of us. We picked out several very pretty outfits and shoes for her little girl which added to her improving mood.

Many times this post-partum or peripartum depression can be overlooked because people may brush it off as a mild "feeling down", tired, or even a little sadness chocked up to no longer being pregnant, a condition known as "the baby blues." This is so much more serious because it can last from weeks to sometimes months leaving the new mother in a debilitating state not able to take care of her newborn, crying often and for no reason, and having panic attacks. When this happens and nothing seems to help, medical attention, including treatment with medication is needed, and care of the baby initiated.

On a personal note, my experience with post-partum or peripartum depression really opened my eyes to an even greater understanding and empathy with those who deal with it. Several years after this event, I suffered a miscarriage of triplets (two boys and one girl) in my second trimester. The whole pregnancy was mismanaged, or we could have saved them. It is a loss that stays with you and haunts you forever. I remember at the time, feeling such a sense of loss, hurt and depression, the crying for no reason, not wanting or unable to get out of bed in the morning and requesting an extension on my sick leave for as long as they let me. I eventually went back to work in a fog and had to push myself to function, double checking everything I did because I felt so unsure of my capability to be efficient in my mental state. It was almost a year later when I got pregnant again that I finally felt like I started to breathe (actually inhale and exhale) again.

This is significant for those of us who work(ed) with pregnant mothers through their delivery and/or family members, particularly husbands to pay attention, be aware of the signs and symptoms and seek help as soon as possible if you notice that it may be more than just the "baby blues" and actually a full-blown case of post-partum or peripartum depression.

There have been stories of mothers drowning their newborn, leaving them outside in extremely hot or cold weather, 'forgetting' to feed them, then getting very angry at their crying. We are so quick to judge these mothers and not pay attention to what is causing these symptoms. I have met women who actually state they hate their newborn and do not want them; this after months of excitement and planning for the baby's arrival. Then I find out that the husband or boyfriend has left — off to be with another woman, or just left and never came back. Unless you have walked in her shoes, there is no way to understand what she is going through.

Several years ago, I had the honor of meeting a well-known calypso singer from the Caribbean. He told me that it was after he had two children of his own and watched the young mother struggle, and go into depression as his career grew and he was away for days at a time performing, while she stayed home with the kids, that he got a glimpse of and had a small understanding of post-partum depression. That led to him writing and singing one of my favorite songs on his album, "Mothers Feel The Pain." You can find it on YouTube under his name — 'Jaunty'. More recently we have heard or read about celebrity wives share their pain of post-partum depression. It can really take you to a dark place that can be hard to come back from. We need to recognize the signs and be supportive, encouraging to seek help. The struggle is real — as one speaking from experience.

Candia Cumberbatch-Lucenius, MHA / RN-Midwife / BSN / CPHM

PLEASE LISTEN TO ME

I have come to you nervous, sick, in pain, sad, and scared

What is wrong? The question goes around in my head.

You look busy, running around doing everything as led,

Getting me settled, hand out meds, and now in a bed.

Can you please slow down now? So much I would like to say.

Everything has changed, I am so scared, in pain night and day.

Will it stop, when will I feel better? Will I get answers today?

All I am asking is that someone listen to me, and I pray.

I just need a minute of your time, but you're still moving I see.

Please, my eyes now pleading, my head feeling heavy as a tree.

Glad you stopped; I explain how I feel, and I am still not pain free.

Better now, and I thank the nurse that stopped to listen to me.

Dedicated to nurses who take the time to
listen to their patients.

©*Candia Cumberbatch-Lucenius, MHA / RN-Midwife / BSN, CPHM.*
November 2020

OUR ELDERLY

When we are young, the elderly either frighten or intrigue us. I can still vividly remember my maternal grandmother Amelida and her sister Maltide when I was growing up. I never even thought of them as 'elderly', they were just Granny and Aunty who we enjoyed spending time with. Granny always seemed like a bitter, old woman who occasionally tried to make her grandchildren happy by during fun things or telling stories. One story we heard often was of losing the love of her life – her husband who we never met, and having to raise eight children on her own. As far I know she never re-married. What I remember of her was her living with her two youngest boys twins up into their forties or fifties.

Aunty, on the other hand lived alone until she got too old to manage on her own, she sold her house and moved in with her brother Paul and his three children – young adults at the time who married and moved out not too long after that. I do not remember meeting Uncle Paul's wife, so know nothing about her. As far as I know Aunty never married either nor had any children. At some point Uncle Paul was too old or sick to look after Aunty and she moved in with Mama. We had all moved out and lived on our own by then. We visited often so got to spend a lot of time with her and listen to her stories of growing up.

When I became a nurse and had the opportunity to work in a

nursing home or take care of geriatric patients I thought of Granny and Aunty. One of the things I enjoyed about working with the elderly is listening to them. They have so much to say, so many stories to tell and we could miss out if we do not slow down and pay attention.

One patient who stands out to me when I worked geriatric nursing was Mrs. Bead. She was a widow, had no children and was admitted by a niece and nephew. Mrs. Bead was sullen and uncooperative most of the time, hardly eating and only responding when absolutely necessary. When I started my shift, it was usually very hectic, handing out medications, and helping clean and feed those who needed assistance. One day I came on duty and got report to find out that Mrs. Bead's roommate had died the previous night. She was despondent, sad, and depressed.

I got through most of my assignment as quickly as possible and decided to sit with Mrs. Bead if she would let me. At first, she didn't seem interested, so I left and returned in about half hour. All I said was "hi Mrs. Bead, just checking on you. Do you need anything?" This time she began to cry even as she shook her head — no. I went up to her and hugged her letting her cry for several minutes. When she stopped, I handed her a few tissues and said, "I have to go check on my other patients, but I will be back." When I got back, Mrs. Bead thanked me and said no one ever has time to listen or talk anymore, and she always felt so alone. I pulled up a chair and sad down saying, "I'm here and I'm listening." My, was I happy I did that! Mrs. Bead shared stories of growing up poor but worked hard and went to college and did very well. She was a retired teacher, met and married her wealthy husband. They had one son who died in a car accident; she wept some more as she spoke about having to bury first her son, then her husband.

What an enlightening conversation about education, politics, racism, police and so much more. I learned so much from Mrs. Bead that day and learned that our elderly have so much to share. The age does not matter – they have lived a long life, have seen and experienced so much and until they can no longer share, we should take time to listen to them, validate their knowledge, allow them to feel useful. When we don't respect their lives, we repress their voices leading to widespread depression.

I allowed Mrs. Bead to 'assist' me by clearing off dirty dishes and getting them to the trolley for housekeeping; she helped wipe off trays, and we kept talking as we 'worked' side by side. You should see the difference that made in her life. She gradually got out of her depression, she felt she like she had some value/worth again. Several years later Mrs. Bead at 99 years old was ready to rest next to her husband and son as she described it. After I took report, I went in to visit her. Smiling weakly she said how happy I had made her last few years, and she was thankful for how I had made her feel useful again. We said good-bye, and she quietly slipped away as I held her hand. With a tear, I whispered "R.I.P. Mrs. Bead".

Candia Cumberbatch-Lucenius, MHA / RN-Midwife / BSN / CPHM

Printed in Great Britain
by Amazon

67004100R00072